"The Book of Mathematics: Volume 3"

SIMONE MALACRIDA

Author's note:

For reasons of printing length, the book has been divided into three volumes.
The first volume covers the first 25 chapters up to and including non-Euclidean geometries as reported in the analytical index of the entire work.
The second volume restarts from real multivariable functions up to chapter 36 dedicated to partial differential equations.
The third volume completes the book.

ANALYTICAL INDEX OF THE WORK

Analytical index

Analytical index

37

INTEGRAL AND INTEGRAL-DIFFERENTIAL EQUATIONS

Introduction and definitions

An integral equation is an equation that presents the unknown under the sign of integral.

Actually, whenever you solve a differential equation, the solution formula is an integral equation, so we have already said a lot about such equations in previous chapters. A linear integral equation has a form like this:

$$y(x) = \lambda \int K(x,z)y(z)dz + f(x)$$

Where $K(x,z)$ is the kernel of the equation (which can be real or complex, symmetric or antisymmetric) and $f(x)$ is the known term.

If $f(x)$ is different from zero we speak of equations of the second kind, if it is equal to zero we speak of equations of the first kind.

Integral equations of Fredholm and Volterra

In integral equations, the integral is defined so we have integration extremes.

If these extremes are fixed we speak of integral equation of Fredholm, if instead one of the extremes is variable in x the equation is called of Volterra.

The Fredholm operator is defined as a bounded linear operator between Banach spaces having a finite-dimensional core and con-core.

Moreover, saying T a Fredholm operator (from a space X to a Y) and S a linear and bounded operator (from the space Y to that X) we have that

$$Id_X - ST$$

$$Id_{Y} - TS$$

are compact operators on X and Y.
The index of a Fredholm operator is defined as follows:

$$indT = \dim \ker T - co\dim ran T = \dim \ker T - \dim coker T$$

The set of Fredholm operators forms an open set in Banach space of bounded and continuous linear operators.
The index of the composition of two Fredholm operators is equal to the sum of the indices of the single operators, furthermore the added Fredholm operator has the opposite index with respect to the starting one.
Finally, given a Fredholm operator and a compact one, their convolution returns again a Fredholm operator having the same index as the starting one.
The tensor product between a Banach space and its dual is a complete space endowed with the following norm:

$$\|X\| = \inf \sum_{\{i\}} \|e_i^*\| \cdot \|e_i\|$$

The space defined by completion with this norm is denoted in this way (called B the generic Banach space) $B^* \tilde{\otimes} B$.
A Fredholm kernel is an element of this projective topological space.
Each nucleus can be associated with a trace and a linear operator of canonical form:

$$tr X = \sum_{\{i\}} \lambda_i e_i^* (e_i)$$

$$L_X f = \sum_{\{i\}} \lambda_i e_i^* (f) \otimes e_i$$

Moreover, every nucleus is called p-summable if the following relation holds:

$$\sum_{\{i\}} |\lambda_i|^p < \infty$$

Fredholm's theory assumes that the Fredholm nucleus is comparable to a Green function, solution of the differential equation:

$$LK(x,z) = \delta(x-z)$$

Where L is a linear differential operator.
Applying this equation to Sobolev spaces and writing the previous equation as an eigenvalue equation:

$$L\psi_n(x) = \omega_n\psi_n(x)$$

An expression of the Fredholm nucleus can be derived:

$$K(x,z) = \sum_n \frac{\psi_n^*(x)\psi_n(z)}{\omega_n}$$

For the inhomogeneous Fredholm equation we can rewrite the known term in this way:

$$f(x) = -\omega y(x)$$

And the solution is given by:

$$y(x) = \frac{1}{K-\omega}\left(\frac{y}{\omega}\right)$$

Using spectral theory, the resolving operator is as follows:

$$R(\omega,x,z) = \frac{1}{K-\omega I} = \sum_n \frac{\psi_n^*(z)\psi_n(x)}{\omega_n - \omega}$$

And the solution is given by:

$$y(x) = \omega\int R(\omega,x,z)y(z)dz$$

Fredholm's theorem provides a sufficient condition for the existence of solutions of Fredholm's equations: the nucleus must be a square summable in a suitable set.
The Fredholm alternative provides a necessary and sufficient condition for the existence of the solutions: the solution must be orthogonal to the

complete set of solutions of the corresponding addition equation i.e. of the Fredholm equation obtained by replacing the Fredholm kernel with its addition and each scalar with its complex conjugate.

In these cases the resolvent can be developed in a power series through the Liouville-Neumann series:

$$R(\lambda) = \frac{1}{I - \lambda \sum_{j=0}^{x} \lambda^j (K^j f)(x)}$$

If the nucleus is continuous, every integral Fredholm equation has a unique solution for any known term and the solution, represented by the Liouville-Neumann series, is uniformly convergent.

The Fredholm determinant is the following:

$$\det(I - \lambda K) = \exp\left[-\sum_n \frac{\lambda^n}{n} tr K^n \right]$$

While the determinant of the resolvent is the so-called Riemann zeta function:

$$\zeta(a) = \frac{1}{\det(I - aK)}$$

An inhomogeneous Fredholm equation of the first type having unlimited integration extrema and kernel defined thus $K(x,z)=K(xz)$ can be seen as the convolution of $K(x,z)$ and $y(z)$ therefore the solution can be written in terms of a Fourier transform or anti-Fourier transform:

$$y(t) = F_\omega^{-1}\left[\frac{F_t[g(t)](\omega)}{F_t[K(t)](\omega)} \right] = \int_{-x}^{x} \frac{F_t[g(t)](\omega)}{F_t[K(t)](\omega)} e^{2\pi i \omega t} d\omega$$

There are other integral and integro-differential equations with which physics is scattered, in particular we can recall Maxwell's equations for electromagnetism, the compressibility equation for statistical mechanics and thermodynamics and Boltzmann's equation for physics statistics.

Calculation of variations

A fundamental field of application of integral equations concerns the calculus of variations, i.e. the search for the extremal points of the functionals.

The fundamental lemma of the calculus of variations states that given a continuous function in an open set and a continuous and continuously differentiable function in the same open set, if the following condition holds:

$$\int_a^b f(x)h(x)dx = 0$$

And the continuous and continuously differentiable function is zero in both extremes, then the other function is zero in the whole set.

Thanks to this lemma it is possible to pass from an integral version of the calculus of variations, such as Hamilton's variational principle, to the resolution of differential equations, such as those of Euler-Lagrange.

Exercises

Exercise 1

Solve the following integral equation:

$$y(t) = \sin(t) + \int_0^t \cos(t - z)y(z)dz$$

Recalling the convolution rule of the Laplace transform:

$$\int_0^t \cos(t - z)y(z)dz = (\cos \star y)(t)$$

We apply the Laplace transform to both sides and exploit the linearity:

$$y(s) = \mathcal{L}\left\{\sin(t)\right\}(s) + \mathcal{L}\left\{(\cos \star y)(t)\right\}(s)$$

Knowing the transform of the sine function and the convolution rule:

$$y(s) = \frac{1}{1+s^2} + \mathcal{L}\left\{(\cos \star y)(t)\right\}(s)$$

$$y(s) = \frac{1}{1+s^2} + \mathcal{L}\left\{\cos(t)\right\}(s)\, y(s)$$

From which:

$$y(s) = \frac{1}{1+s^2} + \frac{s}{1+s^2}\, y(s)$$

Isolating the transform:

$$y(s) = \frac{1}{s^2 - s + 1}$$

Which can be rewritten as:

$$y(s) = \frac{1}{(s-\frac{1}{2})^2 + \frac{3}{4}}$$

At this point, we apply the inverse Laplace transform and we have the solution:

$$y(t) = \sqrt{\frac{4}{3}} e^{t/2} \cos\left(\sqrt{\frac{4}{3}} t\right)$$

Exercise 2

Solve the following integro-differential equation:

$$y'(t) - y(t) = 1 + \sin(t) + 2 \int_0^t (t-z)y(z)dz, \qquad \text{con} \quad y(0) = 1$$

We apply the Laplace transform and remember its linearity:

$$\mathcal{L}\{y'(t)\}(s) + y(s) = \mathcal{L}\{1\}(s) + \mathcal{L}\{\sin(t)\}(s) + 2\mathcal{L}\{(t \star y)(t)\}(s)$$

Recalling the transform of the derivative, of the unit, of the sine and the convolution rule we have:

$$s\,y(s) - 1 + y(s) = \mathcal{L}\{1\}(s) + \mathcal{L}\{\sin(t)\}(s) + 2\mathcal{L}\{(t \star y)(t)\}(s)$$

$$s\,y(s) - 1 + y(s) = \frac{1}{s} + \frac{1}{s^2+1} + 2\mathcal{L}\{(t \star y)(t)\}(s)$$

$$s\,y(s) - 1 + y(s) = \frac{1}{s} + \frac{1}{s^2+1} + 2\mathcal{L}\{t\}(s)\,y(s)$$

$$s\,y(s) - 1 + y(s) = \frac{1}{s} + \frac{1}{s^2+1} + \frac{2}{s^2}\,y(s)$$

We isolate the transform:

$$y(s)\frac{s^3 + s^2 - 2}{s^2} = \frac{1}{s} + \frac{1}{s^2+1}$$

$$y(s) = \frac{1}{(s-1)(s^2+2s+2)}\left(s + \frac{2}{s^2+1}\right)$$

$$= \frac{s^3+s+2}{(s-1)(s^2+2s+2)(s^2+1)}$$

Breaking down the denominator:

$$y(s) = \frac{s^3+s+2}{(s-1)(s+1+\imath)(s+1-\imath)(s+\imath)(s-\imath)}$$

Factoring in simple fractions:

$$y(s) = \frac{A}{s-1} + \frac{B+\imath C}{s+1+\imath} + \frac{B-\imath C}{s+1-\imath} + \frac{D+\imath E}{s+\imath} + \frac{D-\imath E}{s-\imath}$$

The coefficients will be given by:

$$A = \frac{s^3+s+2}{(s^2+2s+2)(s^2+1)}\Bigg|_{s=1} = \frac{2}{5}$$

$$B+\imath C = \frac{s^3+s+2}{(s-1)(s+1-\imath)(s+\imath)(s-\imath)}\Bigg|_{s=-1-\imath} = -\frac{3}{10} + \imath\frac{3}{10}$$

$$D+\imath E = \frac{s^3+s+2}{(s-1)(s+1+\imath)(s+1-\imath)(s-\imath)}\Bigg|_{s=-\imath} = \frac{1}{10} - \imath\frac{3}{10}$$

Therefore:

$$y(s) = \frac{1}{10}\left[\frac{4}{s-1} - 6\frac{s+1}{(s+1)^2+1} + 6\frac{1}{(s+1)^2+1} + 2\frac{s}{s^2+1} - 6\frac{1}{s^2+1}\right]$$

At this point all that remains is anti-transform according to Laplace.

$$y(s) = \frac{1}{10}\left[4e^t + 6e^{-t}(\sin t - \cos t) + 2\cos t - 6\sin t\right]$$

Exercise 3

Find the solution of Fredholm's equation, integral, inhomogeneous, linear and of the II kind:

$$f(x) = \varphi(x) + \lambda \int_a^b dy\, K(x,y)\, f(y),$$

Where lambda is an arbitrary parameter, while:

$$\varphi(x)\ e\ K(x,y)$$

They are given and continuous functions in [a,b]. K(x,y) is called the kernel of the equation and is:

$$|K(x,y| \leq M.$$

In the space C[a,b] consider:

$$g(x) = (Af)(x) = \varphi(x) + \lambda \int_a^b dy\, K(x,y)\, f(y).$$

The definition of distance implies that:

$$\rho(g_1, g_2) = \max |g_1 - g_2| \leq |\lambda|(b-a)\, M\, \rho(f_1, f_2) \implies$$

$$\rho(Af_1, Af_2) \leq |\lambda|(b-a)\, M\, \rho(f_1, f_2).$$

If it happens:

$$\lambda(b-a)M\ <\ 1,$$

The map A is a contraction in the space C[a,b]. This space is complete. By the contraction theorem, the equation presents, for a sufficiently small lambda, one and only one solution given by:

$$f_n(x) = \varphi(x) + \lambda \int_a^b dy\, K(x,y)\, f_{n-1}(y), \qquad n = 1, 2, 3, \ldots$$

Exercise 4

Solve, in the sense of distributions, the following Abel equation:

$$\int_0^x dt \, \frac{u(t)}{(x-t)^\alpha} = g(x), \qquad g(x) \in C^1(\mathbb{R}^+), \quad g(0) = 0, \qquad 0 < \alpha < 1.$$

Recalling Euler's gamma function, Abel's equation can be written as:

$$\Gamma(\beta) f_\beta * u = g(x), \qquad\qquad 0 < \beta = 1 - \alpha < 1.$$

Where is it:

$$f_\alpha(x) = \begin{cases} \dfrac{\vartheta(x) x^{\alpha-1}}{\Gamma(\alpha)}, & \alpha > 0, \\ f'_{\alpha+1}, & \alpha \le 0, \end{cases}$$

And the product given above is the convolution in the sense of distributions.
By the properties of the distributional convolution we have:

$$\Gamma(3) f_{-3} * f_3 * u = f_{-3} * g \implies \Gamma(1-\alpha) u = f_{\alpha-1} * g = f_\alpha * f_{-1} * g = f_\alpha * g'.$$

Using the explicit relation, we get the solution:

$$u(x) = \frac{1}{\Gamma(\alpha)\Gamma(1-\alpha)} \int_0^x dt \, \frac{g'(t)}{(x-t)^{1-\alpha}} = \frac{\sin \pi x}{\pi} \int_0^x dt \, \frac{g'(t)}{(x-t)^{1-\alpha}}.$$

Exercise 5

Using the solver method, find the solution of:

$$\phi(x) = g(x) + \mu \int_0^\pi dt \, \sin x \cos t \, \phi(t), \qquad\qquad g(x) \in C[0, \pi].$$

The first iterated nucleus is null, in fact:

$$K_2(x, t) = \int_0^\pi dy \, \sin x \cos y \sin y \cos t = \frac{1}{2} \sin x \cos t \int_0^\pi dy \, \sin 2y = 0.$$

Therefore the nucleus is orthogonal to itself and the solution is obtained simply by substituting g(x) under the integral sign:

$$\phi(x) = g(x) + \mu \int_0^\pi dt \, \sin x \cos t \, g(t) \, .$$

Exercise 6

Using the contraction method, solve:

$$\phi(x) = B\phi(x) = 1 + 2 \int_0^1 dt \, x^2 \, t \, \phi(t) \, .$$

We note that:

$$|A\phi(x)| = \left| 2x^2 \int_0^1 dt \, t\phi(t) \right| \le 2x^2 \max_{t \in [0,1]} |\phi(t)| \int_0^1 dt \, t \le x^2 \|\phi\| \, ,$$

$$|A^2\phi(x)| \le 2x^2 \int_0^1 dt \, t \, |A\phi(t)| \le 2x^2 \|\phi\| \int_0^1 dt \, t^3 \le \frac{x^2 \|\phi\|}{2} \le \frac{\|\phi\|}{2} \, .$$

Taking the maximum, we have:

$$\|A^2\phi\| \le \frac{\|\phi\|}{2} \quad \Longrightarrow \quad \|B^2\phi_1 - B^2\phi_2\| = \|A^2(\phi_1 - \phi_2)\| \le \frac{\|\phi_1 - \phi_2\|}{2} \, .$$

Operator B is a contraction. Place:

$$\phi_0(x) = 1$$

Is found:

$$\phi_1 = B\phi_0 = 1 + x^2 \, ,$$

$$\phi_2 = B^2\phi_0 = 1 + \frac{3}{2} x^2 \, ,$$

$$\phi_{n+1} = B^{n+1}\phi_0 = 1 + \frac{2^n - 1}{2^{n-1}}x^2$$

$$\implies \phi(x) = \phi_\infty = 1 + 2x^2 .$$

So this function is a fixed point and is the solution.

Exercise 7

Using the resolvent method, calculate:

$$\phi(x) = g(x) + \mu \int_0^1 dt\, xt\, \phi(t) , \qquad\qquad g(x) \in C[0, 1].$$

Place:

$$K_1(x,t) = K(x,t) = xt$$

We have:

$$k = \left[\int_0^1 \int_0^1 dx\, dt\, |K(x,t)|^2 \right]^{1/2} = \frac{1}{3}.$$

The resolvent method can be used if:

$$|\mu| < 3$$

In that case:

$$K_2(x,y) = \frac{xt}{3}, \qquad K_3(x,t) = \frac{xt}{9}, \dots \qquad K_n(x,y) = \frac{xt}{3^{n-1}}$$

$$R(x,t;\mu) = \sum_{n=1}^\infty \mu^{n-1} K_n(x,t) = xt \sum_{n=1}^\infty \left[\frac{\mu}{3}\right]^{n-1} = \frac{3xt}{3-\mu}.$$

The solution is therefore:

$$\phi(x) = g(x) + \frac{3\mu}{3-\mu} \int_0^1 dt \, xt \, g(t) \, .$$

Exercise 8

Find the solution of Volterra's equation using both the contraction method and the resolvent method:

$$\phi(x) = e^x + \int_0^x dt \, e^{x-y} \phi(y) \, .$$

For the contraction method, we take:

$$\phi_0(x) = e^x \, .$$

We have:

$$
\begin{aligned}
\phi_1(x) &= e^x \Big[1 + \int_0^x dy \, e^{-y} \phi_0(y)\Big] = e^x(1+x) \, , \\
\phi_2(x) &= e^x \Big[1 + \int_0^x dy \, e^{-y} \phi_1(y)\Big] = e^x \left(1 + x + \frac{x^2}{2}\right) , \\
\phi_3(x) &= e^x \Big[1 + \int_0^x dy \, e^{-y} \phi_2(y)\Big] = e^x \left(1 + x + \frac{x^2}{2} + \frac{x^3}{3!}\right) , \\
&\cdots \qquad \cdots \\
\phi_n(x) &= e^x \sum_{k=1}^n \frac{x^k}{k!} \quad \Longrightarrow \quad \phi(x) = \phi_\infty(x) = e^{2x} \, .
\end{aligned}
$$

For the resolvent method, we consider the truncated Fredholm kernel:

$$
K_F(x,t) = \begin{cases} e^{x-t}, & t \le x, \\ 0, & t > x, \end{cases}
\quad \Longrightarrow \quad
K_F(t,y) = \begin{cases} e^{t-y}, & t \ge y, \\ 0, & t < y. \end{cases}
$$

The iterated nuclei will be given by:

$$K_1(x, y) \;=\; K_F(x, y),$$

$$K_2(x, t) \;=\; \int_0^x dt\, K_F(x, t) K_1(t, y) = K_F(x, y) \int_y^x dt = (x - y) K_F(x, y),$$

$$K_3(x, t) \;=\; \int_0^x dt\, K_F(x, t) K_2(t, y) = K_F(x, y) \int_y^x (x - t)\, dt = \frac{(x - y)^2}{2} K_F(x, y),$$

$$\cdots$$

$$K_n(x, y) \;=\; \frac{(x - y)^{n-1}}{(n - 1)!} K_F(x, y).$$

And so the solver is:

$$R(x, y; 1) = K_F(x, y) \sum_{n=1}^{\infty} \frac{(x - y)^{n-1}}{n - 1!} = e^{2(x - y)}, \qquad x > y.$$

The solution is therefore:

$$\phi(x) = e^x + \int_0^x dt\, e^{2(x - y)} e^y = e^{2y}.$$

Exercise 9

Calculate eigenvalues and eigenfunctions of the integral equation:

$$\phi(x) = \mu \int_0^1 dy\, K(x, y) \phi(y) = \mu A \phi(x).$$

Where is it:

$$K(x, y) = \begin{cases} x, & x \le y, \\ y, & x \ge y, \end{cases}$$

The nucleus is defined by a bounded function and is square summable in [0,1] x [0,1]. It is also symmetrical. The core can be written as:

$$K(x, y) = \vartheta(y - x)x + \vartheta(x - y)y = K(y, x) \implies$$

$$\begin{cases} K_x''(x, y) = -\delta(x - y)\,, \\ K(0, y) = 0\,, \\ K'(1, y) = 0\,, \\ K'(0, y) = 1\,. \end{cases}$$

The eigenvalues and eigenfunctions are given by:

$$\varphi''(x) + \mu\varphi(x) = 0\,, \qquad \varphi(0) = 0\,, \qquad \varphi'(1) = 0\,, \qquad \varphi'(0) = cost\,.$$

For:

$$\mu \leq 0$$

There are no solutions, while for:

$$\mu > 0$$

There are infinitely many solutions given by:

$$\varphi_n(x) = \sqrt{2}\, \sin\left(n + \frac{1}{2}\right)\pi x\,, \qquad \mu_n = \left(n + \frac{1}{2}\right)^2 \pi^2\,, \qquad n = 0, 1, 2, \dots$$

Exercise 10

Using Fredholm's alternative method, solve:

$$\phi(x) = g(x) + \int_0^\pi dy\, K(x, y)\phi(y)\,,$$

Where is it:

$$g(x) = \sin\frac{3x}{2}\,, \qquad K(x, y) = \begin{cases} \sin x \cos y\,, & x < y\,, \\ \sin y \cos x\,, & x > y\,, \end{cases}$$

The nucleus is defined by a bounded and summable squared function, moreover it is symmetrical. We can rewrite it as:

$$K(x,y) = \vartheta(y-x)\sin x \cos y + \vartheta(x-y)\cos x \sin y \implies$$

$$\begin{cases} K''(x,y) = -K(x,y) - \delta(x-y), \\ K(0,y) = 0, \\ K'(\pi,y) = 0. \end{cases}$$

The eigenvalue equation is given by:

$$\varphi''(x) + [\mu + 1]\varphi(x) = 0, \qquad\qquad \varphi(0) = \varphi'(\pi) = 0,$$

It has solutions only for:

$$\mu + 1 > 0$$

These solutions are:

$$\varphi_n(x) = \sqrt{\frac{2}{\pi}}\sin\left(n+\frac{1}{2}\right)x, \qquad \mu_n = \left(n+\frac{1}{2}\right)^2 - 1, \qquad n = 0,1,2,...$$

We note that, for any n, we have:

$$\mu_n \neq 1$$
$$\lambda_n = 1/\mu_n \neq 1.$$

This means that there is one and only one solution whatever g(x), in fact:

$$g(x) = \sum_{n=0}^{\infty} b_n\varphi_n(x) = \sqrt{\frac{\pi}{2}}\varphi_1(x) \implies b_1 = \sqrt{\frac{\pi}{2}}, \qquad b_n = 0, \qquad \forall n \neq 1.$$

This solution is:

$$\phi(x) = \frac{b_1\varphi_1(x)}{1-\lambda_1} = \frac{\mu_1 b_1\varphi_1(x)}{\mu_1 - 1} = 5\sin\frac{3x}{2}.$$

Exercise 11

Using the degenerate nuclei technique, solve:

$$\phi(x) = x + \int_0^1 dy\, x(x+y)\phi(y)\,,$$

Recall that degenerate nuclei are of the form:

$$K(x,y) = \sum_{k=1}^{N} P_k(x)Q_k(y)\,,$$

Where is it:

$$P_k(x) \in L_2$$

They are linearly independent vectors.
The solution can be written as:

$$\phi(x) = g(x) + \sum_{k=1}^{N} q_k P_k(x)\,,$$

$$\sum_{j=1}^{N} [\delta_{jk} - a_{jk}]q_k = b_j\,,$$

$$\begin{cases} b_k = \int_a^b dx\, Q_k(x)g(x)\,, \\ a_{ij} = \int_a^b dx\, Q_i(x)P_j(x)\,. \end{cases}$$

In our case, we have:

$$K(x,y) = P_1 Q_1 + P_2 Q_2\,,$$
$$P_1 = x\,,\quad P_2 = x^2\,,$$
$$Q_1 = y\,,\quad Q_2 = 1\,.$$

By integrating we get:

$$b_1 = \frac{1}{3}, \qquad b_2 = \frac{1}{2},$$

$$a_{11} = \frac{1}{3}, \qquad a_{12} = \frac{1}{4}, \qquad a_{21} = \frac{1}{2}, \qquad a_{22} = \frac{1}{3}.$$

This leads to the following system:

$$\begin{cases} \frac{2}{3}q_1 - \frac{1}{4}q_2 = \frac{1}{3} \\ -\frac{1}{2}q_1 + \frac{2}{3}q_2 = \frac{1}{2} \end{cases} \implies \begin{cases} q_1 = \frac{25}{23}, q_2 = \frac{36}{23}. \end{cases}$$

The solution is therefore:

$$\varphi(x) = x + \frac{25}{23}x + \frac{36}{23}x^2 = \frac{48}{23}x + \frac{36}{23}x^2.$$

Exercise 12

Find the solutions of:

$$I(u) = \int_{-1}^{1} (u')^2(1 - u')^2 dx$$

With:

$$m = \left\{ u \in C^1([-1,1]) : \quad u(-1) = 0 \quad u(1) = 1 \right\}.$$

Where u satisfies the Euler-Lagrange equation.

The Euler-Lagrange equation is given by:

$$\frac{d}{dx}[2u' + 4u'^3 - 6u'^2] = 0 \quad \Rightarrow \quad 2u' + 4u'^3 - 6u'^2 = C \quad \Rightarrow \quad u' = C_1$$

The only solution that satisfies the conditions at the extremes is:

$$\bar{u}(x) = \frac{x+1}{2}$$

However, this solution is not a minimum, in fact given the sequence:

$$
\begin{aligned}
u_h(x) &= 0 & -1 \le x < -\tfrac{1}{h}\\
u_h(x) &= \tfrac{h}{4}(x + \tfrac{1}{h})^2 & -\tfrac{1}{h} \le x < \tfrac{1}{h}\\
u_h(x) &= x & \tfrac{1}{h} \le x \le 1
\end{aligned}
$$

We have:

$$u_h(-1) = 0$$
$$u_h(1) = 1$$

$$I(u_h) = \frac{1}{16} \int_{-\frac{1}{h}}^{\frac{1}{h}} (1 + h^4 x^4 - 2h^2 x^2)dx = \frac{1}{16}\left(\frac{2}{h} + \frac{2h^4}{5h^5} + \frac{4h^2}{3h^3}\right).$$

Given that:

$$\lim_h I(u_h) = 0,$$

Then m=0. However, the functional I admits minima in the class of piecewise continuous and regular functions, that is, in all those functions which admit a finite number of discontinuities of the first kind in the derivative.
It follows that it is possible to construct infinite functions of this type which satisfy the equation and are minima.

Exercise 13

Find the solutions of the following integral functional which has no solutions in the class of functions C^1 :

$$I(u) = \int_0^1 x(u')^2 dx,$$

With convex integrand function e such that u satisfies the Euler-Lagrange equation with:

$$u(0) = 1 \ e \ u(1) = 0.$$

You will have:

$$(xv')' = 0 \Rightarrow u'(x) = \frac{c}{x} \Rightarrow u(x) = c \log x + d$$

With ced and real constants. There are no class solutions C^1. Also considering that:

$$u_h(x) = 1 \qquad\qquad 0 \le x < \tfrac{1}{h}$$
$$u_h(x) = -\frac{\log x}{\log h} \quad \tfrac{1}{h} \le x \le 1$$
$$u_n(0) = 1 \ e \ u_n(1) = 0$$
$$I(u_h) = \int_{\frac{1}{h}}^{1} \frac{x}{(x \log h)^2} dx = \frac{1}{\log h}$$
$$\lim_n I(u_n) = 0,$$

There are no solutions in the class of piecewise regular functions either.

Exercise 14

Find the extremal of:

$$I(u) = \int_{1}^{2} u'(x)(1 + x^2 u'(x)) dx$$

Where u satisfies the Euler-Lagrange equation and we have:

$$u(1) = 3 \ e \ u(2) = 5$$

Having to satisfy the Euler-Lagrange equation, we have:

$$\frac{d}{dx}(1 + 2x^2 u'(x))dx = 0 \Rightarrow 1 + 2x^2 u'(x) = C$$

And then:

$$u' = \frac{C_1}{2x^2} \Rightarrow u = \frac{1 - C_1}{2x} + C_2$$

Functions are a family of hyperbolas.
Imposing the boundary conditions, we have:

$$C_1 = 9 \ e \ C_2 = 7$$

The extremal is then:

$$u = 7 - \frac{4}{x}$$

Exercise 15

Find the extremal of:

$$I(u) = \int_a^b \frac{\sqrt{1 + u'^2}}{u} dx$$

With:

$$u(a) = A \ e \ u(b) = B$$

We have:

$$\int \frac{du}{\sqrt{(\frac{1}{Cu})^2 - 1}} = \pm (x + C_1)$$

From which:

$$(x + C_1)^2 + u^2 = C_2^2$$

It is a family of circles with center on the abscissa axis. The solution, if it exists, is unique.

Exercise 16

Find the solutions of the functional:

$$I(u) = \int_0^4 (u'^2 - 1)^2 dx$$

Where u satisfies the Euler-Lagrange equation and we have:

$$u(0) = 0 \quad e \quad u(4) = 2.$$

We have that:

$$u'(u'^2 - 1) = C \Rightarrow u' = C$$

So a solution is:

$$u_0(x) = \begin{cases} C_1 x, & 0 \leq x < c \\ C_2 x + (2 - 4C_2), & c \leq x \leq 4 \\ x, & \frac{1}{h} \leq x \leq 1 \end{cases}$$

The function must be continuous in c so:

$$c = \frac{2 - 4C_1}{C_1 - C_2}$$

Moreover:

$$[f_z]_{c-0} = 4C_1(C_1^2 - 1) = [f_z]_{c+0} = 4C_2(C_2^2 - 1)$$

$$[u_0' f_z - f]_{c-0} = (C_1^2 - 1)(3C_1^2 + 1) = [u_0' f_z - f]_{c+} = (C_2^2 - 1)(3C_2^2 + 1)$$

And then:

$$\begin{cases} C_1(C_1^2 - 1) = C_2(C_2^2 - 1) \\ (C_1^2 - 1)(3C_1^2 + 1) = (C_2^2 - 1)(3C_2^2 + 1) \end{cases}$$

Two solutions are obtained. One for:

$$C_1 = 1 \ e \ C_2 = -1$$

And it's:

$$u_1(x) = \begin{cases} x, & -0 \leq x < 3 \\ -x + 6, & 3 \leq x \leq 4 \\ x, & \frac{1}{h} \leq x \leq 1 \end{cases}$$

The other for:

$$C_1 = -1 \ e \ C_2 = 1$$

And it's:

$$u_2(x) = \begin{cases} -x, & -0 \leq x < 1 \\ x - 2, & 1 \leq x \leq 4 \\ x, & \frac{1}{h} \leq x \leq 1 \end{cases}$$

Exercise 17

Using the degenerate nuclei technique calculate:

$$\phi(x) = x + \int_0^\pi dy \, \sin x \cos y \phi(y) \, ,$$

We have:

$$K(x, y) = P_1(x)Q_1(y),$$

$$P_1(x) = \sin x \ , \ Q_1(y) = \cos y.$$

From the definition we get:

$$\begin{cases} b_1 = -2 \\ a_{11} = 0, \end{cases} \implies q_1 = -2 \implies \phi(x) = x - 2\sin x.$$

Exercise 18

Using the degenerate nuclei technique calculate:

$$\phi(x) = x + \int_0^{\pi/2} dy \ \sin x \cos y \phi(y),$$

We have:

$$K(x, y) = P_1(x)Q_1(y),$$

$$P_1(x) = \sin x \ , \ Q_1(y) = \cos y.$$

From the definition we get:

$$\begin{cases} b_1 = \frac{\pi}{2} - 1 \\ a_{11} = \frac{1}{2}, \end{cases} \implies q_1 = \pi - 2 \implies \phi(x) = x + (\pi - 2)\sin x.$$

Exercise 19

Calculate eigenvalues and eigenfunctions of the integral equation:

$$\phi(x) = \mu \int_0^1 dy \ K(x, y)\phi(y) = \mu A\phi(x).$$

With:

$$K(x, y) = \begin{cases} i, & x \le y, \\ -i, & x \ge y, \end{cases}$$

The nucleus is bounded, summable and symmetrical.
It can be written as:

$$K(x, y) = i\vartheta(y - x) - i\vartheta(x - y) = \bar{K}(y, x), \quad \Longrightarrow$$

$$\begin{cases} K'_x(x, y) = -2i\delta(x - y), \\ K(0, y) = -K(1, y) = i. \end{cases}$$

The inverse operator is a first-order differential operator such that:

$$\varphi'(x) - 2i\mu\varphi(x) = 0, \qquad\qquad \varphi(0) + \varphi(1) = 0.$$

Whose general solution is:

$$\varphi(x) = cost\, e^{2i\mu x}$$

The normalized eigenfunctions are:

$$\varphi_n(x) = e^{2i\mu_n x}, \qquad \mu_n = \left(n + \frac{1}{2}\right)\pi, \qquad n \in \mathbb{Z}.$$

Exercise 20

Using Fredholm's alternative, solve:

$$\phi(x) = g(x) + \int_0^\pi dy\, K(x, y)\phi(y),$$

$$g(x) = 0, \qquad K(x, y) = \begin{cases} \sin y \cos x, & x < y. \\ \sin x \cos y, & x > y. \end{cases}$$

The nucleus is bounded, summable and symmetrical.
It can be written as:

$$K(x, y) = \vartheta(y - x) \cos x \sin y + \vartheta(x - y) \sin x \cos y \quad \Longrightarrow$$

$$\begin{cases} K''(x, y) = -K(x, y) + \delta(x - y), \\ K(\pi, y) = 0, \\ K'(0, y) = 0. \end{cases}$$

The equation that determines the eigenvalues is:

$$\varphi''(x) + [1 - \mu]\varphi(x) = 0, \qquad\qquad \varphi(\pi) = \varphi'(0) = 0,$$

Which has solution only for:

$$1 - \mu > 0.$$

We therefore have:

$$\varphi_n(x) = \sqrt{\frac{2}{\pi}} \cos\left(n + \frac{1}{2}\right) x, \qquad \mu_n = 1 - \left(n + \frac{1}{2}\right)^2, \qquad n = 0, 1, 2, \ldots$$

All eigenvalues are different from 1 and therefore the solution is unique
for any g(x).
Since g(x)=0 the solution is:

$$\phi(x) = 0.$$

38

SPECTRAL THEORY

Definitions

Let H be a Hilbert space. In the following we will always assume that H is a complex space.

We consider the dot product and the space of continuous linear operators on H .

Given an operator A belonging to this space, we shall say that a complex number belongs to the resolving set of A if there exists another operator B belonging to the same space such that:

$$(\lambda I - A)B = B(\lambda I - A) = I$$

Where I denotes the identity operator.

This is equivalent to requiring that:

$$(\lambda I - A)$$

Let be a bijective function of H itself, with B its inverse function (linear and continuous).

The set of complex numbers that do not belong to the resolving set of A is called the spectrum of A and is denoted by the Greek letter sigma.

The set of all operators B defined as the complex number varies within the solving set is called the solving family of A.

Given an operator belonging to a space of linear and continuous operators on a Hilbert space, it proves that:

- the spectrum of A is a non-empty, closed and bounded subset of the complex plane.

- the function below is analytic within the resolving family of A

$$\lambda \to \left\langle (\lambda I - A)^{-1} x, y \right\rangle$$

- defined the spectral radius as:

$$r(A) = \sup_{\lambda \in \sigma(A)} |\lambda|$$

The following formula holds:

$$r(A) = \lim_{n \to \infty} \left\| A^n \right\|^{\frac{1}{n}}$$

For each linear and continuous operator one can define its adjoint (also linear and continuous) such that:

$$\left\| A^* A \right\| = \left\| A \right\|^2$$

If A coincides with its adjoint, then the operator is said to be self-adjoint.
For a self-adjoint operator, the spectral radius coincides with the norm.
A consequence of this is that the norm of a linear and continuous operator is given by:

$$\left\| A \right\| = \sqrt{r(AA^*)}$$

A linear and continuous operator is said to be unitary if it has an inverse which is equal to its adjoint.
The following properties hold for unitary operators:

$$\left\| Ux \right\| = \left\| x \right\|$$
$$\left\langle Ux, Uy \right\rangle = \left\langle x, y \right\rangle$$

A linear and continuous operator is said to be an orthogonal projection equal to its square and its addition.

A Hermitian form on H is a function B which associates a complex number to each pair of vectors belonging to the Hilbert space.
This function has the following properties:

$$B(x_1 + x_2, y) = B(x_1, y) + B(x_2, y)$$
$$B(x, y_1 + y_2) = B(x, y_1) + B(x, y_2)$$
$$B(\alpha x, y) = \alpha B(x, y)$$
$$B(x, \alpha y) = \overline{\alpha} B(x, y)$$

A Hermitian form is said to be bounded if there exists a constant M such that:

$$|B(x, y)| \leq M \|x\| \cdot \|y\|$$

If A is a linear and continuous operator, then the following Hermitian form is bounded:

$$B(x, y) = \langle Ax, y \rangle$$

Furthermore, if the Hermitian form is bounded, the linear and continuous operator is unique and its norm is bounded.

A linear operator A in H is a linear map to values in H defined on a vector subspace of H, called the domain of A.
A linear operator A is said to be symmetric if the domain is dense and the adjunct operator is an extension of A.
Every self-adjoint operator is symmetric.
A symmetric operator is self-adjoint if and only if the domain of the operator coincides with the domain of the adjoint operator.
Operators formed by orthonormal bases are called diagonals.
Called A a self-adjoint linear operator, if there exists a real number in the resolvent of A such that:

$$(A - \lambda_0 I)^{-1}$$

It is compact, so A is a diagonal operator.
It follows that self-adjoint operators with compact inverse are diagonal.

To conclude this first part, we provide two practical examples of operators. The momentum operator in quantum mechanics is a self-adjoint operator. In particular, by defining the domain of this operator as the Sobolev space $H^1(R)$ (i.e. the space of functions which, together with their first

1153

derivatives in the distributional sense, belong to the space $L^2(R)$), we see that this space is dense and its functions are absolutely continuous and tend to zero indefinitely.

The momentum operator is defined as follows:

$$(Af)(x) = i\frac{df}{dx}(x)$$

Another example of a symmetric and self-adjoint operator is given by the Laplace operator.

It is defined in a multidimensional Sobolev space $H^2(R^n)$.
The operator is explicit as follows:

$$Af = -\Delta f = -\sum_{i=1}^{n}\frac{\partial^2 f}{\partial x_i^2}$$

By the known formulas of Green we have that:

$$\langle Af, g \rangle = \langle f, Ag \rangle$$

Spectrum classification

Given a (bounded or unbounded) linear operator A in H, the following equation generates the classification of the spectrum:

$$Ax - \lambda x = y$$
$$\lambda \in C, y \in H, x \in D(A)$$

When the parameter varies, four distinct cases can arise.

FIRST CASE
The operator

$$A - \lambda I$$

It is bijective and its inverse is continuous for the norm in H.

In this case, lambda belongs to the resolving set. The solution exists and is unique.

SECOND CASE
The operator

$$A - \lambda I$$

It's not injective.
Lambda is an eigenvalue. The set of eigenvalues is called the point spectrum of A.
Every non-zero solution of the starting equation is called an eigenvector. The eigenvectors are infinite, in fact they enjoy the property of linear combinations.

THIRD CASE
The operator

$$A - \lambda I$$

It is injective and its image is a dense subspace in H, but different from H. In this case, lambda belongs to the continuous spectrum of A.
The solution of the starting equation is unique.

FOURTH CASE
Unless one falls back into the three previous cases, lambda belongs to the residual spectrum of A.

Each case listed excludes the others, therefore the sets of solutions are disjoint and their union gives the entire complex field.
A linear operator in H is said to be closed if for each sequence of vectors belonging to its domain and for each pair of vectors belonging to H we have:

$$x_n \rightarrow x \Rightarrow Ax_n \rightarrow y$$
$$x \in D(A)$$
$$y = Ax$$

Every linear and continuous operator is closed.
Every self-adjoint operator is closed.
For self-adjoint operators, the residual spectrum is empty.

Riesz theorem

We define a function with bounded variation as follows.

$$F : [a,b] \to C \mid F(t) = F_1(t) - F_2(t) + iF_3(t) - iF_2(t)$$
$$t \in [a,b]$$

Where the various subfunctions are real, increasing and continuous to the right.

Riesz's theorem states that given a closed and bounded interval [a,b] and a linear and continuous operator A, then there exists a unique function F with bounded variation in the interval such that:

$$A(f) = \int_a^b f(t)dF(t)$$

$$\left| \int_a^b f(t)dF(t) \right| \le \|A\| \cdot \|g\|_\infty$$

$$f \in C([a,b]), g \in B([a,b])$$

In essence, Riesz's theorem states that a functional is represented by a single function with bounded variation (hence the general definition of Riesz's representation theorem).

Functions of self-adjoint operators

Calling A a self-adjoint continuous operator in H, we construct the following polynomial with generally complex coefficients:

$$p(A) = a_0 A^n + \ldots + a_{n-1}A + a_n I$$

This polynomial has the following properties:

$$p(t)=t \Rightarrow p(A)=A$$
$$p(t)=1 \Rightarrow p(A)=I$$
$$r(t)=p(t)+q(t) \Rightarrow r(A)=p(A)+q(A)$$
$$r(t)=p(t) \cdot q(t) \Rightarrow r(A)=p(A) \cdot q(A)$$
$$(\alpha p)(A)=\alpha p(A)$$
$$\overline{p}(A)=p(A^*)$$

If now instead of the polynomial, we want to consider a generic function of a self-adjoint continuous operator, we arrive at the following theorem.
Given a continuous, self-adjoint linear operator in a complex separable Hilbert space, there exists a unique function, which is a homomorphism, with the following properties:

$$\|\phi(f)\| = \|f\|_\infty$$
$$f(t)=t \Rightarrow \phi(f)=A$$
$$f(t)=\frac{1}{\mu-t} \Rightarrow \phi(f)=(\mu I - A)^{-1}$$

The following Weierstrass theorem also holds.
Given a compact set contained in R, then for every continuous function which sends this set to C, there exists a sequence of polynomials which converge uniformly to this function.
A consequence of Weierstrass' theorem is the following lemma:
given a generic polynomial in te another expressed for the continuous and self-adjoint linear operator A we have:

$$\|p(A)\| = \|p\|_\infty$$

Non-negative operators

An operator is said to be non-negative if it happens that:

$$\langle Ax, x \rangle \geq 0$$

If A is a self-adjoint continuous linear operator, defined a function that is a homomorphism and that satisfies the conditions set forth in the previous theorem, we have:

$$f \geq 0 \Rightarrow \phi(f) \geq 0$$

The function then transforms non-negative continuous functions into non-negative operators.

The following notable relations hold.

If A is a non-negative self-adjoint operator then the spectrum of A consists of non-negative numbers.

If A is a non-negative self-adjoint operator then there is a unique non-negative self-adjoint operator equal to the square root of A.

In an analogous way we can define the fractional powers of a non-negative self-adjoint operator.

Given two self-adjoint operators we will say that one is greater than or equal to the other if their difference is a non-negative self-adjoint operator.

This defines a partial ordering among the self-adjoint operators.

The spectral theorem

Called A a self-adjoint continuous linear operator in a complex and separable Hilbert space, in the first chapter we saw how it is possible to make a linear and continuous operator correspond to every continuous function.

The spectral theorem, which we are going to state, extends all this to an operator that is also unlimited.

We define B(R) as the space of functions leading from R to C, which are bounded, measurable (according to the Lebesgue measure) and endowed with the following norm:

$$\|f\|_\infty = \sup_{t \in R} |f(t)|$$

The spectral theorem states that for a self-adjoint linear operator (even unbounded) there exists a function that sends from B(R) to L(H) which is a homomorphism and with the following properties:

$$\|\varphi(g)\| \le \|g\|_{\infty}$$

$$g_n(t) \to g(t), \sup_n \|g_n\| < \infty \Rightarrow \varphi(g_n)x \to \varphi(g)x$$

$$g_n, g \in B(R), x \in H$$

Furthermore, if A is continuous and the function f is continuous on an interval containing the spectrum of A, we have:

$$\varphi(f) = \phi(f)$$

There are generalizations of this theorem in which the operator A is not self-adjoint, but only normal.

This theorem allows us to construct functions of the operator A for a fairly large class of functions.

To understand how to construct such a function, it is necessary to move on to concepts of spectral measurement

Spectral and integral measurements

We define spectral measure as a family of linear and continuous operators E(t) in H such that measure is a self-adjoint projection with the following properties:

$$E(t)E(s) = E(\min(t, s))$$

$$\lim_{t \to +\infty} E(t)x = x$$

$$\lim_{t \to -\infty} E(t)x = 0$$

$$\lim_{t \to s^+} E(t)x = E(s)x$$

From this it follows that the operators E(t) commute and that the function of the inner product defined by E(t) on x is non-negative, increasing and right-continuous.

Furthermore, the function given by the inner product defined by E(t)x on y has limited variation.

We define an operator given by the integral of bounded and measurable functions with respect to the spectral measure:

1159

$$\int_R f(t)dE(t)$$

We therefore have that:

$$\int_R f(t)d\langle E(t)x, y\rangle = \lim_{a\to\infty} \int_{-a}^{a} f(t)d\langle E(t)x, y\rangle$$

$$\left|\int_R f(t)d\langle E(t)x, y\rangle\right| \le C_1 \|f\|_\infty \|x\| \|y\|$$

Given a spectral measure, the linear and continuous operator given by the integral thus defined exists and is unique.
This operator is limited.

Spectral measurement of an operator

Calling A a self-adjoint operator, if the spectral theorem holds then the spectral measure of A is given by:

$$E(t) = \varphi(\chi_{(-\infty, t]})$$

Where the function in parentheses is 1 in the interval considered and zero elsewhere.
It can easily be verified that this function satisfies the properties stated in the previous paragraph for spectral measurements.
That said, we can give a second definition of the spectral theorem, based on the spectral measurements.
Let A be an also unbounded self-adjoint operator and E(t) its spectral measure.
For each function f belonging to B(R), we have:

$$\varphi(f) = \int_R f(t)dE(t)$$

$$\|\varphi(f)x\|^2 = \int_R |f(t)|^2 d\langle E(t)x, x\rangle$$

From this follows the following remarkable corollary.

Under the same hypotheses of the spectral theorem just stated in its new form, for every function f belonging to B(R) there exists and is unique a linear and continuous operator which satisfies the following relation:

$$\left\langle \int_R f(t)dE(t)x, y \right\rangle = \int_R f(t)d\left\langle E(t)x, y \right\rangle$$

This operator is a homomorphism with the following properties:

$$\left\| \phi(f) \right\|^2 = \int_R \left| f(t) \right|^2 d\left\langle E(t)x, x \right\rangle$$

$$\left\| \int_R f(t)dE(t) \right\| \leq \left\| f \right\|_\infty$$

$$f_n(t) \to f(t), \sup_n \left\| f_n \right\|_\infty < \infty \Rightarrow \int_R f_n(t)dE(t)x \to \int_R f(t)dE(t)x$$

Furthermore, if A is continuous and the function f is continuous on an interval that contains the spectrum of A, we have that:

$$\phi(f) = \int_R f(t)dE(t)$$

From these results, we can derive a further theorem which links the spectral measurement and the operators.
Given a self-adjoint operator, if a spectral measure E(t) satisfies this condition, then the spectral measure of the operator itself is exact:

$$\left\langle (\mu I - A)^{-1}x, x \right\rangle = \int_R \frac{1}{\mu - t} d\left\langle E(t)x, x \right\rangle$$

With these results, one can think of defining an integral (Stieltjes) operator. Indeed, given a self-adjoint operator and its corresponding spectral measure, the spectrum of A is compact and therefore there exists an open bounded interval (a,b) which contains this spectrum.
Under these hypotheses there exists an integral defined as follows:

$$\int_a^b t dE(t)$$

This integral coincides with A and therefore it is an integral in the operator sense.

Stone's theorem

The state of a physical system at a given instant of time can be described by a suitable vector belonging to a Hilbert space, generally a space of complex-valued functions.

The time evolution of the system can be described by a function with values in that space.

If the knowledge of the state in any instant of time allows us to determine the evolution of the system in all the following states, we have that:

$$U(t)u_0 = u(t, u_0)$$

In other words, the function U(t) describes the time evolution of the system from a fixed state to a subsequent one.

The initial condition will be given by:

$$U(0) = I$$

If the laws governing the system do not change over time, we have that:

$$U(t+s) = U(t) + U(s)$$

A family of functions with such characteristics is called a group of operators.

If the individual functions are unitary then the group of operators is said to be unitary.

The unitary group U is said to be strongly continuous if:

$$\lim_{t \to s} U(t)x = x$$

A consequence of the properties of the group is that the operators commute, i.e. we have that:

$$U(t)^{-1} = U(t)^* = U(-t)$$

Given a strongly continuous group U of unitary operators, the infinitesimal generator of U is the operator given by:

$$Bx = \lim_{t \to 0} \frac{U(t)x - x}{t}$$

The domain of B is defined as the set of vectors for which this limit exists in the norm of H and Bx is properly the value of this limit.

Given an infinitesimal generator B of a strongly continuous group U of unitary operators in H, it is shown that the following Cauchy problem:

$$\begin{cases} u'(t) = Bu(t) \\ u(0) = u_0 \end{cases}$$

It has only one solution given by:

$$u(t) = U(t)u_0$$

In addition, the following property on norms holds:

$$\|u(t)\| = \|u_0\|$$

Thus we can state Stone's theorem.

An operator B in H is an infinitesimal generator of a strongly continuous group U of unitary operators if and only if A=-iB is self-adjoint.

In that case, we have:

$$U(t) = \int_R e^{it\lambda} dE(\lambda)$$

Where the function E is the spectral measurement associated with A.

The formula is written like this:

$$U(t) = e^{itA} = e^{tB}$$

As we shall see, Stone's theorem has important physical applications.

Application: Schrodinger equation

Schrodinger's equation is as follows:

$$\frac{1}{i}\frac{\partial}{\partial t}\psi(t,x) = -\Delta\psi(t,x) + V(x)\psi(t,x)$$

The unknown function has complex values and depends on both the temporal and spatial (multidimensional) variable.
The function V instead has real values and is known.
The initial condition of this partial differential equation is the following:

$$\psi(0,x) = \psi_0(x)$$

The solution of Schrodinger's equation is called a wave function and completely describes the physical state of a given system at a given time.
The square modulus of the wave function is the probability density of finding the particle at point x at time t therefore the wave functions must satisfy the following normalization condition:

$$\int_{R^n} |\psi(t,x)|^2 dx = 1$$

In addition to the normalization condition and being solutions of the Schrodinger equation with its initial condition, the wave functions belong to the Sobolev space $H^2(R^n)$ and their derivative exists in the norm of $L^2(R^n)$:

$$\frac{\partial}{\partial t}\psi(t,x) = \lim_{h\to 0}\frac{\psi(t+h,x) - \psi(t,x)}{h}$$

If V is bounded and measurable and the initial condition can be normalized and belongs to the aforementioned Sobolev space, the solution of the Schrodinger equation exists and is unique.
We can define in $L^2(R^n)$ such an operator:

$$Af(x) = -\Delta f(x) + V(x)f(x)$$

We show that this operator is self-adjoint.
In conclusion, this means that for various forms of the potential V(x) it is possible to apply everything studied by the spectral theory for the resolution of the Schrodinger equation.

It is therefore possible to define a spectrum of the operator A, its spectral measure and to apply the spectral theorem and that of Stone for the physical systems described by the Schrodinger equation.

The operative vision allows to completely untie quantum mechanics from the formalism of the matrices or from that of wave mechanics, generating a wider class of solutions.

Application: harmonic oscillator

To mathematically describe a harmonic oscillator, we consider a self-adjoint operator A defined in $L^2(R)$:

$$Af(x) = -\frac{d^2}{dx^2}f(x) + x^2 f(x)$$

We look for solutions to the following eigenvalue problem:

$$\lambda f(x) = -\frac{d^2}{dx^2}f(x) + x^2 f(x)$$

The solutions are given by:

$$e_n(x) = c_n e^{\frac{1}{2}x^2}\frac{d^n}{dx^n}e^{-x^2}$$

$$c_n = (2^n n!)^{-\frac{1}{2}}(-1)^n \pi^{-\frac{1}{4}}$$

$$\lambda = 2n+1$$

$$n = 0,1,2,...$$

These functions belong to $L^2(R)$ and are a complete orthonormal basis of this space.

The numerical coefficients chosen ensure that each function has a unitary norm.

We can therefore define the operator A as a diagonal operator:

$$Af(x) = \sum_{n=0}^{\infty} (2n+1)\langle f, e_n \rangle e_n(x)$$

Whose domain is given by:

$$D(A) = \left\{ f \in L^2(R) : \sum_{n=0}^{\infty} (2n+1)^2 \left| \langle f, e_n \rangle \right|^2 < \infty \right\}$$

The equation describing the time evolution of a quantum harmonic oscillator is given by:

$$\frac{1}{i} \frac{\partial}{\partial t} \psi(t,x) = -\frac{\partial^2}{\partial x^2} \psi(t,x) + x^2 \psi(t,x)$$

Whose solutions are:

$$\psi(t,x) = e^{itA} \psi_0(x) = \sum_{n=0}^{\infty} e^{it(2n+1)} \langle \psi_0, e_n \rangle e_n(x)$$

which satisfy the normalization condition.

39

MATHEMATICS AND DISCRETE GEOMETRY

Discrete mathematics deals with the study of discrete quantities, over all countable sets.

A topological space has a discrete topology when all its subsets are open or, equivalently, when all its subsets are closed or when all its points are open. The discrete topology is the one with the greatest degree of finesse of all topologies, the opposite is the trivial topology.

A metric space having a discrete metric has a definite distance equal to zero if the elements coincide and equal to one if the elements are different. The discrete topology is therefore metrizable and satisfies all separation axioms.

A discrete space is totally disconnected, homogeneous and is compact if and only if it is finite.

Up to homeomorphisms, discrete spaces are classified by their cardinality: it follows that every countable discrete space is homeomorphic to the set of relative numbers.

Discrete geometry is concerned with the study of geometric objects by determining their discrete and combinatorial properties.

A result of discrete geometry is Pick's theorem: in a simple polygon whose vertices have integer coordinates, called i the number of integer coordinate points inside the polygon and p the number of integer coordinate points on the perimeter of the polygon, the area of the polygon is given by Pick's formula:

$$A = i + \frac{p}{2} - 1$$

Another result of discrete geometry is the formulation (and demonstration) of Kepler's conjecture according to which, given spheres in three-dimensional Euclidean space, there is no way to arrange them with an average density higher than that obtained using cubic geometry a centered faces or the hexagonal one.

Another aspect of discrete geometry is the resolution of triangulation problems.

Thanks to discrete mathematics it is possible to generalize many geometric properties of solids, in particular of polyhedra by defining the combinatorial structure as the set of its vertices, its edges and its faces and their respective incidence relationships.

In addition, it is also possible to define its metric structure, i.e. in terms of discrete metric spaces.

It can be seen how a rotation around an axis of symmetry or a translation leaves the metric and combinatorial structures unaltered, while a homothety transforms only the metric structure.

Generalizing to the n-dimensional Euclidean space R, the analog of the polygon in the plane and of the polyhedron in space is defined as the n-dimensional polytope.

As with most Euclidean geometry, the study focuses on convex polytopes; in particular, the convex closure of a finite set of points is called V-polytope, while H-polytope is the intersection of half-spaces of a bounded n-dimensional space R.

The dimension of a convex polytope is the dimension of the minimum subspace that contains it, while two convex polytopes are said to be affine isomorphic if there is a bijective affine transformation between the two spaces that contain them.

40

FRACTAL GEOMETRY

Introduction

Fractal geometry deals with objects, called fractals, with internal homothety.
This property is called self-similarity and guarantees that, on whatever scale the fractal is observed, the object always has the same global characteristics.
A fractal is not constructed with a function described in suitable coordinates, but with an algorithm, typically recursive.
Based on the equation that defines the algorithm, linear, non-linear or random fractals can be defined.

The Hausdorff dimension of a metric space is the number of balls of maximum radius r needed to completely cover the metric space.
This dimension is the threshold value below which the Hausdorff measure in those dimensions is infinite and above which the measure is zero.
For any subset B of the metric space X, the Hausdorff dimension defined on a ball A is as follows:

$$H^s_\delta(B) = \inf\left\{ \sum_{i=1}^{\infty} diam(A_i)^s \right\}$$

The exterior Hausdorff dimension of the metric space is:

$$H^s(B) = \lim_{\delta \to 0} H^s_\delta(B)$$

The following equality holds only if B and C are disjoint and Borel sets:

$$H^s(B \cup C) = H^s(B) + H^s(C)$$

All Borel subsets of the metric space are measurable, and the exterior Hausdorff dimension is a countable, additive measure.
The Hausdorff dimension of an n-dimensional Euclidean space R is just n, that of the circle of unit radius is one, while countable sets have Hausdorff dimension zero.

Given a topological space, the topological dimension is the smallest integer n for which every open cover has a refinement in which every point is contained in at most n+1 sets.
An n-dimensional Euclidean space R has topological dimension n, a graph having a finite number of vertices and edges has topological dimension one.
For fractals the Hausdorff dimension is always greater than the topological dimension.

The Minkowski-Boulingand dimension determines the dimension of a set S in a metric space.
Given N(x) the number of cells of lateral length x needed to cover the set, then the Minkowski-Boulingand dimension is defined as follows:

$$\dim{}_{MB}(A) = \lim_{x \to 0} \frac{\log N(x)}{\log\left(\dfrac{1}{x}\right)}$$

If such limit does not exist, then we speak of upper and lower dimension which correspond to the upper and lower bound of the expression.
The Minkowski-Boulingand dimension is always greater than or equal to the Hausdorff dimension.
These two dimensions are the most common fractal dimensions.

Types of fractals

The Mandelbrot set is a fractal that is a subset of the complex plane, defined as follows:

$$M = \left\{ c \in C : \sup_{n \in N} \left| f_c^n(0) \right| < \infty \right\}$$

$$f_c(z) = z^2 + c$$

If the modulus of the generic complex number is greater than 2, the sequence diverges and therefore the point is outside the Mandelbrot set.
Given a holomorphic function in complex analysis, a Julia set is a set of all points whose behavior is chaotic after repeated iterations.
The Julia set is connected if the point belongs to the Mandelbrot set.
If the complex function is defined like this:

$$f_c(z) = \left(\left|\operatorname{Re}(z)\right| + i\left|\operatorname{Im}(z)\right|\right)^2 + c$$

Then a new fractal arises, called a burning ship.

The Cantor set is a subset of the real interval [0,1] obtained recursively by removing a central open segment at each step: for example, in the first step the open sub-interval between 1/3 and 2 is eliminated /3.
The Cantor set has zero Lebesgue measure and, at the same time, it is an uncountable set, endowed with the cardinality of the continuum.
Furthermore it is a closed subset of the interval [0,1], it is compact, each of its points is of accumulation, its internal part is empty and it is a totally disconnected set.
The Cantor set is a fractal whose Hausdorff dimension is as follows:

$$H^s = \frac{\ln 2}{\ln 3}$$

The Cantor dust is a multi-dimensional version of the Cantor set obtained by multiplying the Cantor set with itself a finite number of times at the level of the Cartesian product.
The Cantor dust is a particular Cantor space, ie a topological space homeomorphic to the Cantor set.
A Cantor space is generated by a topological product of a countable number of Cantor sets.
Given a topological space, it is Cantor space if and only it is non-empty, each of its points is of accumulation, it is compact, it is totally disconnected, it is metrizable and it has the cardinality of the continuum.
The Cantor function is a function that generalizes the Cantor set to the functional scope.
This function is continuous and increasing, but has zero derivative almost everywhere, as it is constant in all sub-intervals of [0,1].

The Koch curve is a fractal curve which is constructed with a recursive algorithm very similar to the one used for the Cantor set.
Each segment is divided into three equal parts, the central segment is canceled and replaced with two identical segments which become two

sides of an equilateral triangle, then the same mechanism is carried out for all the segments.

This curve is continuous, has infinite length, is self-similar (as a fractal) and cannot be derived at any point.

A particular Koch curve is the Peano curve, ie a curve, parametrized by a continuous function that completely covers a square starting from the interval [0,1].

This function is therefore surjective and it can be seen how it coincides with the Cantor function: the consequence of this is that the Peano curve is not injective nor differentiable.

Other fractal curves are the Sierpinski curves which are a sequence of n continuous closed plane curves.

As n tends to infinity, these curves fill the unit square and hence the Hausdorff dimension is two.

The Euclidean length is equal to:

$$l_n = \frac{2(1+\sqrt{2})}{3} 2^n - \frac{2-\sqrt{2}}{3 \cdot 2^n}$$

The Sierpinski carpet is a fractal that is obtained by starting from a square, dividing it into nine smaller equal squares, removing the central square and iterating the algorithm for all the existing squares.

This fractal is a closed, limited and compact whole, it has the cardinality of the continuum and a zero Lebesgue measure.

Furthermore, it has topological dimension equal to one and is a universal planar curve. The Hausdorff dimension is as follows:

$$H^s = \frac{\log 8}{\log 3}$$

If instead of the square we have a triangle divided into four equal and smaller triangles we obtain the Sierpinski triangle which has Hausdorff dimension:

$$H^s = \frac{\log 3}{\log 2}$$

A three-dimensional version of the Sierpinski carpet is the fractal called Menger sponge.

In this case we start from a cube and divide it into 27 equal sub-cubes, always eliminating the central one.
Each of the six faces of Menger's sponge is a Sierpinski carpet.
The topological dimension of the Menger sponge is equal to one, the Hausdorff one is as follows:

$$H^s = \frac{\log 20}{\log 3}$$

All the fractals presented so far are deterministic. The random fractals are, for example, the random walk and the Brownian motion (which has a Hausdorff dimension equal to two).
For all fractals it is possible to draw up a list based on the increasing value of the Hausdorff dimension.
The complete calculation of fractals is possible only thanks to the computing power of computers while their use is extended to scientific disciplines such as statistics, physics and chemistry.

41

NUMERICAL CALCULATION

Introduction

Numerical calculation studies the mechanisms for solving mathematical problems that are based on numerical algorithms, i.e. on logical processes that do not tend to find a solution at the level of formulas (also called analytical) but rather build methods for the approximate calculation of the numerical value in itself.

The application fields of numerical calculus are varied, in particular the calculation of the solutions of a transcendent equation that cannot be solved analytically or the calculation of the roots of any polynomial or the calculation of particular values of a function are of primary importance.

The vast majority of algorithms related to numerical computation are iterative.

Calculation of the roots of a polynomial

A first large category of numerical methods consists in calculating the roots of a polynomial or of a generic transcendental function.

Horner's algorithm allows us to evaluate a polynomial by carrying out N additions and N multiplications, instead of the normal N additions and $N(N+1)/2$ multiplications required.

We have to rewrite any polynomial in another equivalent form:

$$P_N(x) = a_N + a_{N-1}x + ... + a_1 x^{N-1} + x^N = a_N + x(a_{N-1} + x(a_{N-2} + ... + x(a_1 + x)...))$$

The value of the polynomial is calculated in this recursive form:

$$p_0 = 1$$
$$p_{k-1} = p_k x + a_{k-1}$$
$$0 \le k \le N-1$$

The simplest method for finding the roots of an equation is given by the bisection method or dichotomous method.
This method assumes that if a function assumes values with different signs in a given interval then the root of this function is included in that interval. This result is known as the zeros theorem and is valid under suitable conditions.
In formulas we have:

$$f(a) \cdot f(b) < 0 \Rightarrow \exists c \in [a,b]: f(c) = 0$$

The bisection method divides the interval between a and b in half.
If in the middle of the interval the function is null, then that value is the root sought.
In the opposite case, the same algorithm is applied recursively considering only the half of the interval where there is still inversion of the sign.
At the n-th step, the approximation on the real value of the root is given by:

$$|e_n| \leq \frac{b-a}{2^{n-1}}$$

One method that varies the size of the interval is the linear interpolation method.
Instead of always taking half of the given interval, we take an intermediate value given by a weighted average:

$$c = \frac{a \cdot f(b) - b \cdot f(a)}{f(b) - f(a)}$$

In Muller's method a second order polynomial is used as an interpolating function.
An historical method for the numerical calculation of the value of a function in a given point is given by the method of false position in Fibonacci (or regula falsi) which always applies the bisection method, but the interval in which to find the root is calculated according to proportional criteria.
A better method for calculating the roots of a function is given by the so-called method of tangents (or Newton's method).
By drawing the curve corresponding to the function on a Cartesian plane, this method consists in substituting, in a determined point, the geometric tangent in place of the curve itself and assuming as an approximate value

of the root the value of the abscissa of the point given by the intersection between tangent and the abscissa axis.

Resolutions of matrix systems

Another large class of numerical methods is that relating to the calculation of solutions of linear systems, especially as regards matrix notation.

Gauss's elimination method, also called MEG, is a numerical algorithm used to determine the solutions of a system of linear equations and to calculate the rank of a matrix as well as its inverse matrix.

Using Gauss moves it is possible to reduce a matrix to a step matrix, i.e. to a matrix in which the first non-zero element of a row must be further right than the first non-zero element of the previous row.

Considering a complete matrix describing a system of linear equations, we can modify this matrix according to Gauss's three moves: either swap two rows or multiply a row by a number other than zero or add a row to a multiple of another row.

Gauss's algorithm states that if the first row of the complete matrix has a null first element, then we swap it for a row whose first element is non-zero.

For every other row, different from the first, whose first element is not null, the first row is multiplied by a coefficient such that the sum between the first row and the chosen row has the first null element.

The third point of Gauss's algorithm is given by iteration: in fact, by applying the first two points, the first column has all the digits equal to zero (except the first which can assume any value).

At this point, we can iterate Gauss' algorithm on the submatrix obtained by deleting the first row and first column until we obtain a step matrix which is the irreducible form.

By doing so, the inverse of any matrix is easily computed, assuming it exists.

The QR decomposition of a square matrix is a decomposition of the type: M=QR, where Q is an orthogonal matrix and R an upper triangular matrix. By applying this factorization to a linear system Ax=b, we have the solutions of this system:

$$x = R^{-1}(Q^T b)$$

If A is an invertible matrix, then the so-called LU decomposition can be applied.

Calling P a permutation matrix, L a lower triangular matrix with unit diagonal and U an upper triangular matrix, we have

$$PA = LU$$

An application of this decomposition is given by the calculation of the inverse matrix, in fact from simple matrix notations we obtain:

$$A^{-1} = U^{-1}L^{-1}P$$

Another application is given by the calculation of the determinant.
Said S the number of permutations and denoted by uel the elements of the matrices U and L:

$$\det A = (-1)^{S} \prod_{i=1}^{n} u_{ii} l_{ii}$$

If instead A is a square, Hermitian and positive definite matrix it can be decomposed according to the Cholesky algorithm into a triangular matrix multiplied by its conjugate transpose.

$$A = L(L^{T})^{*}$$

If A is real and symmetric the conjugate transpose coincides with the transpose.
Cholesky's algorithm is always inspired by Gauss's algorithm.
Defined A the matrix of the linear system and M an invertible matrix, if A=MN the recursive solutions of the system are given by:

$$x^{k-1} = M^{-1}(Nx^{k} + b)$$

Jacobi's method considers M to be the diagonal matrix having the same diagonal as A:

$$x^{k-1} = D^{-1}((A - D)x^{k} + b)$$

In the Gauss-Seidel method M=L, lower triangular matrix and N=U, upper triangular matrix with zero diagonal. The solutions are therefore:

$$x^{k-1} = L^{-1}(Ux^{k} + b)$$

A variant of this method is given by the so-called SOR or overrelaxation method
If we consider the solution given by the Gauss-Seidel method at the k-th iterative step and a particular relaxation parameter, the solution is given by:

$$x^{k+1} = \omega x_{gs}^{k+1} + (1 - \omega)x^k$$

Exercises

Exercise 1

Determine, as alpha>0 varies, the condition number, normally infinite, of the matrix:

$$A = \begin{pmatrix} 1 + \alpha & 1 \\ -1 & -1 \end{pmatrix}.$$

The inverse of A is given by:

$$A^{-1} = \frac{1}{\alpha} \begin{pmatrix} 1 & 1 \\ -1 & -1 - \alpha \end{pmatrix},$$

You get:

$$\mu_\infty(A) = \|A\|_\infty \|A^{-1}\|_\infty = (2 + \alpha)\frac{2 + \alpha}{\alpha} = \alpha + 4 + \frac{4}{\alpha}.$$

The function tends to infinity as alpha tends to zero.
The function tends to infinity as alpha tends to infinity.
The function has a minimum for alpha=2.
Optimal conditioning occurs in this case.
The function is well conditioned if alpha does not assume values too high or too close to zero.

Exercise 2

Data:

$$T = \begin{pmatrix} -2 & 2 & 7 \\ 0 & 4 & 2 \\ 0 & 0 & 0.5 \end{pmatrix}, \qquad b = \begin{pmatrix} 1 \\ -2 \\ 3 \end{pmatrix},$$

Solve Tx=b and compute the inverse of T using the back substitution method.

The determinant of T is -4.
We have:

$$x_3 = \frac{3}{0.5} = 6$$

$$x_2 = \frac{-2 - 2 * x_3}{4} = -3.5$$

$$x_1 = \frac{1 - 2 * x_2 - 7 * x_3}{-2} = 17$$

Therefore:

$$\begin{pmatrix} -2 & 2 & 7 \\ 0 & 4 & 2 \\ 0 & 0 & 0.5 \end{pmatrix} \begin{pmatrix} x_1 \\ x_2 \\ x_3 \end{pmatrix} = \begin{pmatrix} 1 \\ 0 \\ 0 \end{pmatrix} \implies \begin{array}{rcr} x_3 &=& 0 \\ x_2 &=& 0 \\ x_1 &=& -0.5 \end{array}$$

$$\begin{pmatrix} -2 & 2 & 7 \\ 0 & 4 & 2 \\ 0 & 0 & 0.5 \end{pmatrix} \begin{pmatrix} y_1 \\ y_2 \\ y_3 \end{pmatrix} = \begin{pmatrix} 0 \\ 1 \\ 0 \end{pmatrix} \implies \begin{array}{rcr} y_3 &=& 0 \\ y_2 &=& 0.25 \\ y_1 &=& 0.25 \end{array}$$

$$\begin{pmatrix} -2 & 2 & 7 \\ 0 & 4 & 2 \\ 0 & 0 & 0.5 \end{pmatrix} \begin{pmatrix} z_1 \\ z_2 \\ z_3 \end{pmatrix} = \begin{pmatrix} 0 \\ 0 \\ 1 \end{pmatrix} \implies \begin{array}{rcr} z_3 &=& 2 \\ z_2 &=& -1 \\ z_1 &=& 6 \end{array}$$

So the inverse is:

$$T^{-1} = \begin{pmatrix} -0.5 & 0.25 & 6 \\ 0 & 0.25 & -1 \\ 0 & 0 & 2 \end{pmatrix}.$$

Exercise 3

Calculate with the Gaussian method Ax=b with:

$$A = \begin{pmatrix} 2 & -4 & 1 \\ 6 & -14 & 8 \\ -2 & 0 & 6 \end{pmatrix} \qquad b = \begin{pmatrix} 1 \\ -1 \\ 1 \end{pmatrix}$$

With Gauss's method, we reduce ourselves to a triangular system in this way:

$$(A|b) = \begin{pmatrix} 2 & -4 & 1 & 1 \\ 6 & -14 & 8 & -1 \\ -2 & 0 & 6 & 1 \end{pmatrix} \quad (II - 3I), \quad (III + I) \Longrightarrow$$

$$\begin{pmatrix} 2 & -4 & 1 & 1 \\ 0 & -2 & 5 & -4 \\ 0 & -4 & 7 & 2 \end{pmatrix} \quad (III - 2II) \Longrightarrow$$

$$\begin{pmatrix} 2 & -4 & 1 & 1 \\ 0 & -2 & 5 & -4 \\ 0 & 0 & -3 & 10 \end{pmatrix}.$$

The solutions are therefore:

$$x_3 = -\frac{10}{3}$$

$$x_2 = -\frac{-4 - 50/3}{2} = -\frac{19}{3}$$

$$x_1 = \frac{1 + 10/3 - 76/3}{2} = -\frac{21}{2}.$$

Exercise 4

Approximate with the Jacobi method Ax=b where:

$$A = \begin{pmatrix} 12 & -4 & 1 \\ 6 & -16 & 8 \\ -2 & 0 & 6 \end{pmatrix} \qquad b = \begin{pmatrix} 18 \\ -20 \\ -16 \end{pmatrix}$$

The matrix A is diagonal dominant and the Jacobi method converges.
The iteration matrix is given by:

$$J = \begin{pmatrix} 1/12 & 0 & 0 \\ 0 & -1/16 & 0 \\ 0 & 0 & 1/6 \end{pmatrix} * \begin{pmatrix} 0 & 4 & -1 \\ -6 & 0 & -8 \\ 2 & 0 & 0 \end{pmatrix} = \begin{pmatrix} 0 & 1/3 & -1/12 \\ 3/8 & 0 & 1/2 \\ 1/3 & 0 & 0 \end{pmatrix}.$$

And the iteration vector:

$$q = D^{-1} * b = \begin{pmatrix} 3/2 \\ 5/4 \\ -8/3 \end{pmatrix}.$$

We have:

$$x_0 = \begin{pmatrix} 1 & 0 & -1 \end{pmatrix}^t$$

And then:

$$x_1 = \begin{pmatrix} 1/12 + 3/2 \\ -1/8 + 5/4 \\ 1/3 - 8/3 \end{pmatrix} = \begin{pmatrix} 19/12 \\ 9/8 \\ -7/3 \end{pmatrix} \approx \begin{pmatrix} 1.5833 \\ 0.6250 \\ -2.3333 \end{pmatrix}$$

$$x_2 = \begin{pmatrix} 41/72 + 3/2 \\ -55/96 + 5/4 \\ 19/36 - 8/3 \end{pmatrix} = \begin{pmatrix} 149/72 \\ 65/96 \\ -77/36 \end{pmatrix} \approx \begin{pmatrix} 2.0694 \\ 0.6771 \\ -2.1389 \end{pmatrix}$$

$$x_3 = \begin{pmatrix} 349/864 + 3/2 \\ -169/576 + 5/4 \\ 149/216 - 8/3 \end{pmatrix} = \begin{pmatrix} 1645/864 \\ 571/576 \\ -427/216 \end{pmatrix} \approx \begin{pmatrix} 1.9039 \\ 0.9566 \\ -1.9769 \end{pmatrix}.$$

The method converges to the following solution:

$$x = \begin{pmatrix} 2 \\ 1 \\ -2 \end{pmatrix};$$

Exercise 5

Find the least squares parabola for:

x	1	2	3	4	5
y	0.5	0	-0.5	1	0.75

We want to find:

$$y = \alpha + \beta x + \gamma x^2$$

Where the coefficients are least squares solutions of the system:

$$\begin{pmatrix} 1 & 1 & 1 \\ 1 & 2 & 4 \\ 1 & 3 & 9 \\ 1 & 4 & 16 \\ 1 & 5 & 25 \end{pmatrix} \begin{bmatrix} \alpha \\ \beta \\ \gamma \end{bmatrix} = \begin{bmatrix} 0.5 \\ 0 \\ -0.5 \\ 1 \\ 0.75 \end{bmatrix}.$$

Moving on to the normal equations:

$$\begin{pmatrix} 5 & 15 & 55 \\ 15 & 55 & 225 \\ 55 & 225 & 979 \end{pmatrix} \begin{bmatrix} \alpha \\ \beta \\ \gamma \end{bmatrix} = \begin{bmatrix} 1.75 \\ 6.75 \\ 30.75 \end{bmatrix}.$$

Whose solution is:

$$\alpha = 23/20, \ \beta = -129/140 \text{ e } \gamma = 4895/27412.$$

Exercise 6

Consider in the range [-1,2]

$$f(x) = \frac{(x+2)^2}{(x-3)}$$

Find the interpolating polynomial in Lagrange form at the nodes -1,0,0.5,2.

We have:

$$f(-1) = -0.25, \quad f(0) = -4/3,$$
$$f(0.5) = -2.5 \text{ e } f(2) = -16.$$

The Lagrange interpolating polynomial has degree at most 3 and is given by:

$$p_3(x) = \sum_{i=0}^{3} L_i(x)f(x_i),$$

Where is it:

$$L_0 = \frac{(x-x_1)(x-x_2)(x-x_3)}{(x_0-x_1)(x_0-x_2)(x_0-x_3)} = \frac{x(x-0.5)(x-2)}{(-1)(-1.5)(-3)}$$

$$= -\frac{2}{9}\left(x^3 - \frac{5}{2}x^2 + x\right)$$

$$L_1 = \frac{(x-x_0)(x-x_2)(x-x_3)}{(x_1-x_0)(x_1-x_2)(x_1-x_3)} = \frac{(x+1)(x-0.5)(x-2)}{(1)(-0.5)(-2)}$$

$$= x^3 - \frac{3}{2}x^2 - \frac{3}{2}x + 1$$

$$L_2 = \frac{(x-x_0)(x-x_1)(x-x_3)}{(x_2-x_0)(x_2-x_1)(x_2-x_3)} = \frac{(x+1)(x)(x-2)}{(1.5)(0.5)(-1.5)}$$

$$= -\frac{8}{9}(x^3 - x^2 - 2x)$$

$$L_3 = \frac{(x-x_0)(x-x_1)(x-x_2)}{(x_3-x_0)(x_3-x_1)(x_3-x_2)} = \frac{(x+1)(x)(x-0.5)}{(3)(2)(1.5)}$$

$$= \frac{1}{9}\left(x^3 + \frac{1}{2}x^2 - \frac{1}{2}x\right).$$

Therefore:

$$p_3(x) = -\frac{5}{6}x^3 - \frac{5}{4}x^2 - \frac{3}{2}x - \frac{4}{3},$$

Exercise 7

With the bisection method, approximate in the interval [-2,1] the zero of:

$$f(x) = xe^{-x} + e,$$

Zero is given by an alpha value in the range.
Also the function is continuous and therefore the method is applicable.
Sayings:

$$a_0 = -2 \text{ e } b_0 = 1:$$

We have the first iteration step:

$$c_0 = \frac{a_0 + b_0}{2} = -0.5$$

Where the range is large:

$$|b_0 - a_0| = 3.$$

The error estimate and true error are:

$$\frac{|b_0 - a_0|}{2} = 1.5.$$
$$|c_0 - \alpha| = 0.5.$$

Since:

$$f(c_0) = -0.5e^{0.5} + e > 0$$

Is found:

$$\begin{aligned} a_1 &= a_0 = -2 \\ b_1 &= c_0 = -0.5 \end{aligned}$$

At this point we can iterate the reasoning to obtain:

$$c_1 = \frac{a_1 + b_1}{2} = -1.25$$

$$|b_1 - a_1| = 1.5$$
$$\frac{|b_1 - a_1|}{2} = 0.75.$$
$$|c_1 - \alpha| = 0.25.$$
$$f(c_1) = -1.25e^{1.25} + e < 0,$$
$$\begin{aligned} a_2 &= c_1 = -1.25 \\ b_2 &= b_1 = -0.5 \end{aligned}$$

And so on.

Exercise 8

Given the function:

$$f(x) = x^3 - 4x,$$

Calculate its root in the interval [1.5,2.5] using the two functional iteration methods:

$$\begin{cases} x_{i+1} &= g(x_i) \\ g(x) &= x - \frac{f(x)}{kx} \end{cases}, \quad k = 4, 8,$$

Given that:

$$g(x) = x - \frac{x^2}{k} + \frac{4}{k},$$

$$g'(x) = 1 - \frac{2x}{k}.$$

The two methods are convergent if:

$$|g'(x)| < 1 \quad \Leftrightarrow \quad -1 < 1 - \frac{2x}{k} < 1 \Leftrightarrow \quad 0 < x < k.$$

Being k=4 ok=8 the two methods converge.
We have for the first method (k=4):

$$x_1 = x_0 - \frac{x_0^2}{4} + 1 = \frac{31}{16} \approx 1.9375$$

$$x_2 = x_1 - \frac{x_1^2}{4} + 1 = \frac{2047}{1024} \approx 1.9990$$

$$x_3 = x_2 - \frac{x_2^2}{4} + 1 = \frac{8388607}{4194304} \approx 1.99999998$$

With the second method:

$$x_1 = x_0 - \frac{x_0^2}{8} + \frac{1}{2} = \frac{55}{32} \approx 1.71878$$

The speed of convergence of the first method is quadratic, in fact:

$$\lim_{i \to \infty} \frac{x_{i+1} - 2}{(x_i - 2)^2} = \lim_{x_i \to 2} \frac{x_i - 2 - x_i^2/4 + 1}{(x_i - 2)^2} = \lim_{x_i \to 2} \frac{4 - x_i - 2}{4(x_i - 2)} = -\frac{1}{4}.$$

While that of the second is linear:

$$\lim_{i \to \infty} \frac{x_{i+1} - 2}{x_i - 2} = \lim_{x_i \to 2} \frac{x_i - 2 - x_i^2/8 + 0.5}{x_i - 2} = \lim_{x_i \to 2} 1 - \frac{x_i + 2}{8} = \frac{1}{2}.$$

Exercise 9

With the string method, approximate the zero of the function in the interval [-1,2].

$$f(x) = \log(1 + x^2) + 3x.$$

Said alpha the value of zero, we have:

$$f'(x) = \frac{3x^2 + 2x + 3}{1 + x^2},$$

The derivative is positive in the interval.
Moreover,

$$f''(x) = \frac{2(1 - x^2)}{(1 + x^2)^2},$$

And so the first derivative has a maximum at x=1.
Therefore, to ensure sufficient convergence conditions, the ropes to be used must have angular coefficient:

$$m > \frac{1}{2}f'(1) = 2.$$

The method becomes:

$$x_{i+1} = x_i - \frac{f(x_i)}{m},$$

Or:

$$x_{i+1} \;=\; x_i - \frac{\log(1 + x_i^2) + 3x_i}{m}.$$

Choosing:

$$m = 2.5, \; x_0 = 0.5$$

Is found:

x_0	x_1	x_2	x_3	x_4
0.500	$0.107 * 10^{-1}$	$0.210 * 10^{-2}$	$0.418 * 10^{-3}$	$0.836 * 10^{-4}$

The speed of convergence is linear, in fact:

$$\lim_{i \to \infty} \frac{x_{i+1} - 0}{x_i - 0} = \lim_{x_i \to 0} \frac{x_i - 2\log(1 + x_i^2)/5 - 6x_i/5}{x_i} =$$

$$\lim_{x_i \to 0} -\frac{1}{5} - \frac{2\log(1 + x_i^2)}{5x_i} = -\frac{1}{5},$$

Exercise 10

Approximate the zero of the function in the interval [1.5,3] with the tangent method.

$$f(x) = 0.5x - e^{x-2}$$

We have:

$$f'(x) = 0.5 - e^{x-2} < 0 \quad \text{su } I,$$
$$f''(x) = -e^{x-2} < 0 \quad \forall x;$$

The sufficient conditions of convergence impose that, given alpha as the root, we have:

$$x_0 \in (\alpha, 3],$$

If we choose just 3 we have:

$$x_{i+1} \;=\; x_i - \frac{f(x_i)}{f'(x_i)},$$

$$x_{i+1} \;=\; \frac{e^{x_i-2}(1 - x_i)}{0.5 - e^{x_i-2}}.$$

From which:

x_0	x_1	x_2	x_3	x_4	x_5
3	2.4508	2.1290	2.0142	2.0002	2.0000

The rate of convergence is quadratic.

.

42

NUMERICAL ANALYSIS

Introduction

Numerical analysis constitutes a sector of mathematics that is complementary to all the rest.

The importance of this analysis affects aspects of algebra, matrix mathematics, mathematical analysis, differential equations and many mathematical problems.

The advent of computers has then given a great boost to this sector, above all for the immense computing power available and the consequent results, which now span every application field.

Interpolation of functions

A first class of numerical methods is that relating to the interpolation and extrapolation of functions, following a discretization procedure which characterizes the transition from the continuum of mathematical analysis to the discrete of numerical analysis.

The linear extrapolation of a given point, with respect to its neighbors, is given by the following relationship:

$$y(x_*) = y_{k-1} + \frac{x_* - x_{k-1}}{x_k - x_{k-1}} (y_k - y_{k-1})$$

This extrapolation is essential for applications of linear regression.

A basic idea of polynomial interpolation is to express any function as an approximation of high order polynomials.

However, this idea is contraindicated on the basis of Runge's phenomenon, which demonstrates how, in some cases, the linear interpolation error tends to infinity.

A first method to reduce this error, as the degree of polynomial increases, is to use the Cebichev nodes instead of equidistant points for the interpolation.
These nodes are defined as follows:

$$x_i := \cos\left(\frac{2i-1}{2n}\pi\right)$$

Where n is the degree of the polynomial and ei is an integer between 1 and n.
These points are the roots of the Cebichev polynomials:

$$T_n = \cos(n\vartheta)$$

These polynomials are the solutions of the Cebichev differential equation:

$$(1-x^2)y'' - xy' + n^2 y = 0$$

Another way to reduce the polynomial interpolation error is to use spline functions.
These functions consist of sets of polynomials connected to each other so that, in a given interval, they are continuous with continuous derivatives, at least up to a certain order of derivation.
The connection points between polynomials are called spline nodes, and polynomial interpolation with spline functions is called spline interpolation.
Through this mechanism, Runge's phenomenon does not occur.

Definitions

We give below some definitions that will be useful throughout the numerical analysis.
Numerical stability is a property which guarantees the limitation of the error, but at the same time the non-cancellation of the error itself.
In other words, a numerical algorithm will be stable if its approximation error with respect to the real case is a finite number or an infinitesimal, but not zero.
If this error becomes zero, the phenomenon of numerical cancellation occurs.
Conditioning is a measure of the ratio of error to data uncertainty.

A problem is well conditioned when the solution, under small perturbations, does not vary much from the solution to the original problem.
Conversely, the problem is ill-conditioned.
Examples of conditioning numerical problems are given by the numerical calculation of the roots of a polynomial or by the numerical solution of systems of equations or matrices.
There are several ways to measure the conditioning of a numerical problem, for example in fluid dynamics the Peclet number is used, even if generally a good conditioning number is the spectral one, related to the two norm, calculated as the ratio between the spectral radius and the minimum of the solving eigenvalues.
This ratio is always greater than one, as it grows we have a measure of the bad conditioning of the problem.
Connected to the problem of numerical cancellation and conditioning is the concept of inherent error, i.e. the error that is committed by representing a real number, in particular irrational numbers or periodic rational numbers, with a finite number of digits, as happens in all practical cases, from calculators to manual calculation.
Assuming that the error on the initial data is given by:

$$\varepsilon_x = \frac{(x_p - x_r)}{x_r}$$

The inherent error can be expressed as:

$$\varepsilon_y = \frac{|f(x_p) - f(x_r)|}{|f(x_r)|}$$

If it is much greater than the initial error, then the problem is ill-conditioned.

Discretization of the integral

Another major area of numerical analysis is that of discretizing the operations of mathematical analysis.
Numerical integration consists in calculating a definite integral without analytically calculating the primitive.
There are many numerical methods for calculating the numerical integral.

Newton-Cotes formulas assume that the value of the function to be integrated is known in a series of equidistant points.
The closed form of these formulas also considers the ends of the integration interval, the open one does not.
For the closed form there is this relationship:

$$\int_{a}^{b} f(x)dx \approx \sum_{i=0}^{n} w_i f(x_i)$$

Each point is spaced by a quantity called pitch, while the multiplicative coefficients are called weights and come from Lagrange polynomials. The open form can be expressed as follows:

$$\int_{a}^{b} f(x)dx \approx \sum_{i=1}^{n-1} w_i f(x_i)$$

The trapezium rule is a closed Newton-Cotes formula which considers a pitch equal to:

$$\frac{h}{2}(f_0 + f_1)$$

and has an error given by:

$$-\frac{h^3}{12} f^{(2)}(\xi)$$

This rule can be expressed as follows:

$$\int_{a}^{b} f(x)dx \approx (b - a)\frac{f(a) + f(b)}{2}$$

Another rule that can be derived from the closed Newton-Cotes formulas is the Cavalieri-Simpson rule, also known as the method of parabolas. The step and the error are defined as follows:

$$\frac{h}{3}(f_0 + 4f_1 + f_2)$$

$$-\frac{h^5}{90} f^{(4)}(\xi)$$

As you can see, this rule is more precise than that of the trapezoid.
The rule is therefore:

$$\int_a^b f(x)dx \approx \frac{h}{3}\left[(y_0 + 4y_1 + y_2) + (y_2 + 4y_3 + y_4) + ... + (y_{n-2} + 4y_{n-1} + y_n)\right]$$

There are other more precise rules that can be obtained from closed Newton-Cotes formulas such as Boole's rule.
From the open Newton-Cotes formulas we obtain the rectangle rule, also known as the midpoint rule, which has pitch and error given by:

$$2hf_1$$

$$\frac{h^3}{24} f^{(2)}(\xi)$$

This rule can be expressed as:

$$\int_a^b f(x)dx \approx (b-a) f\left(\frac{a+b}{2}\right)$$

As for the closed Newton-Cotes formulas, also for the open ones there are other rules that reduce the error, such as Masina's rule.
Furthermore, the rectangle rule can be composed with other rules.
The major problem of the Newton-Cotes formulas lies in the fact that, for many large n, one can observe Runge's phenomenon.
Therefore, other more stable methods of numerical integration are needed, among these there is the quadrature of Gauss.
This method considers n+1 nodal points in the integration interval that are the zeros of an orthogonal polynomial with respect to a weight function and interpolates the integral with this formula:

$$\int_a^b f(x)w(x)dx = \sum_{i=0}^n f(x_i)w_i$$

As in the case of the Newton-Cotes formulas, the weight functions can be expressed on the basis of the coefficients of the Lagrange polynomials:

$$\int_a^b l_i(x)w(x)dx$$

The calculation of integrals of functions of several variables uses advanced methods, among which the Monte Carlo numerical methods.

Finite difference method

The numerical approximation of the derivative passes from the concept of finite difference.
It can be expressed like this:

$$\forall c, h \in R \Rightarrow \Delta_{c,h} f(x) = f(x + c + \frac{h}{2}) - f(x + c - \frac{h}{2})$$

Where c is the center eh is the pitch of the difference.
There are three types of finite difference, the centered one, the forward one and the backward one, defined as follows:

$$\Delta_0 f(x) = f(x + \frac{h}{2}, h) - f(x - \frac{h}{2})$$
$$\Delta_h f(x) = f(x + h) - f(x)$$
$$\Delta_{-h} f(x) = f(x) - f(x - h)$$

It is also possible to define operators to the differences which exploit the previous definitions, which are linear and respond to the Leibnitz rule. For example, the forward difference operator is given by:

$$\Delta_h = T_h - I$$
$$T_h(f) = f(x + h)$$

Where I is the identity. The n-th order finite differences are expressed as follows:

$$\Delta^n_h f(x) = \sum_{i=0}^{n} (-1)^i \binom{n}{i} f(x + (n-i)h)$$

$$\Delta^n_{-h} f(x) = \sum_{i=0}^{n} (-1)^i \binom{n}{i} f(x - ih)$$

$$\Delta^n_0 f(x) = \sum_{i=0}^{n} (-1)^i \binom{n}{i} f(x + (\frac{n}{2} - i)h)$$

Finite differences are fundamental for numerically approximating a derivative.

Thus we have centered forward and backward numerical derivatives.

For example, for the first derivative we have:

$$f'(x_i) \approx \frac{f(x_{i+1}) - f(x_{i-1})}{2h}$$

$$f'(x_i) \approx \frac{f(x_{i+1}) - f(x_i)}{h}$$

$$f'(x_i) \approx \frac{f(x_i) - f(x_{i-1})}{h}$$

The substitution of the analytic derivatives with finite differences gives rise to the method of finite differences which is the main numerical method for solving ordinary differential equations.

This method causes an ordinary differential equation to become a difference equation that can be solved both in numerical terms and using discrete analytical tools, such as the zeta transform.

Difference methods are defined as one-step if the n+1-th value depends only on the n-th value, otherwise it is called multi-step.

The one-step difference method that exploits the forward finite differences is called explicit Euler method, the one that exploits the backward finite differences is called implicit Euler method, whose generic solution formula is given by:

$$y_{n+1} = y_n + hf(x_{n+1}, y_{n+1})$$

Other one-step methods are the trapezium method, also called Crank-Nicholson:

$$y_{n+1} = y_n + \frac{h}{2}(f_n + f_{n+1})$$

Heun's:

$$y_{n+1} = y_n + \frac{h}{2}(f(x_n, y_n) + f(x_n + h, y^{(0)}_{n+1}))$$

$$y^{(0)}_{n+1} = y_n + hf_n$$

And the Euler exponential:

$$y_{n+1} = e^{-Bh}y_n + B^{-1}(1 - e^{-Bh})A$$

Which holds if the differential equation is of the form:

$$y'(t) = A - By(t)$$

Multistep methods are given by the Adams-Bashforth one:

$$y_{n+1} = y_n + \frac{h}{12}(23f_n - 16f_{n-1} + 5f_{n-2})$$

And from that of Adams-Moulton:

$$y_{n+1} = y_n + \frac{h}{12}(5f_{n+1}8f_n - f_{n-1})$$

The Runge-Kutta methods are instead a family of one-step numerical iterative methods for solving ordinary differential equations, in particular for Cauchy problems.
The definition interval of the Cauchy problem is divided evenly according to the following step:

$$h = \frac{t_f - t_0}{n}$$

These methods state that the numerical resolution of a Cauchy problem is given by:

$$
\begin{cases}
y_{n+1} = y_n + h\sum_{i=1}^{s} b_i f(t_n + \vartheta_i h, Y_i) \\
Y_i = y_n + h\sum_{j=1}^{s} a_{ij} f(t_n + \vartheta_j h, Y_j) \\
i = 1,\ldots,s
\end{cases}
$$

Where in the summations there are the quadrature formulas on the nodes that contain the respective weights, as already explained previously for other numerical methods.

Furthermore, there are numerical methods for solving differential equations which exploit the numerical approximations of power series.

Numerical methods are said to be convergent if the numerical solution approximates the exact solution for a step tending to zero:

$$
\lim_{h\to 0^+} \max_{n=0,1,\ldots,[\frac{t^*}{h}]} \left\| y_{n,h} - y(t_n) \right\| = 0
$$

While they are said to be consistent if the truncation error tends to zero for a step that tends to zero:

$$
\lim_{h\to 0} \frac{\delta_{n+k}^h}{h} = 0
$$

Finally the order p of a numerical method is defined as follows (for a step tending to zero):

$$
\delta_{n+k}^h = O(h^{p+1})
$$

Finite element method

A method for the numerical solution of partial differential equations is given by the finite volume method.

Basically it is a question of dividing the integration domain into a finite number of volumes and of integrating the equations in these volumes with boundary conditions defined on the boundaries of each single volume.

This method represents a simplification of a much more widespread method which is that of finite elements.

The first phase of this method consists in modeling the mathematical problem using a differential equation, generally with partial derivatives.

The modeling starts from the assumption that the real case neglects some parameters considered non-fundamental while focusing on others, obviously depending on the boundary conditions.

The second phase passes through the discretization of the finite element model both in space and in time to bring the system from an infinite number of degrees of freedom to a finite number, all to be processed numerically.

In this discretization phase, other errors are generated which must not affect either the stability or the consistency of the solutions found on the basis of this method.

A finite element is distinguished by its dimension (one, two or three dimensional), by the nodes which are precise points which identify its geometry, by the degrees of freedom (the values which the functions and their gradients in the nodes can assume) and by the forces on the nodes, which take into account the support reactions and the boundary conditions on the nodes.

The fundamental procedure that distinguishes finite elements from other numerical methods is the mapping of the space, also called mesh, which is never a uniform mapping, but which uses calculation algorithms to adapt to the individual models examined from time to time.

Therefore, the finite elements are almost never evenly distributed.

In many cases it is necessary to introduce pre-conditioning of the model to guarantee the stability of the solution and this is done using matrix methods of elementary numerical analysis, for example the pre-conditioning matrices, also called stiffness matrices.

The finite element method is based on the Galerkin scheme, i.e. on the weak formulation of partial differential equations.

Therefore, to guarantee the existence and uniqueness of the solution, the Lax-Milgram lemma becomes fundamental which requires that, in this equation, the form a(u,v) is bilinear and coercive:

$$\forall v \in V \Rightarrow a(u,v) = l(v)$$

Where V is a generic Hilbert space.

Galerkin's method decomposes the discretization of this problem into finding a solution in a sequence of subspaces such that we have:

$$\{V_n\}_{n=1}^{-\infty} \subset V$$

$$\bigcup_{n=1}^{-\infty} V_n = V$$

In each of these finite-dimensional subspaces the initial problem can be solved exactly from the discrete point of view.
We therefore have that the general problem on infinite-dimensional spaces reduces to finding n solutions of discrete problems on finite-dimensional spaces in this way:

$$\forall v \in V_n \Rightarrow a(u_n, v) = l(v)$$

At this point it is enough to remember that every solution can be expressed as a linear combination of a basis of the subspace:

$$u_n = \sum_{j=1}^{N_n} U_j v_j$$

By defining three matrices that respectively condense the solutions, the boundary conditions and the coefficients:

$$K_n = \{s_{ij}\}_{i,j=1}^{N_n}$$

$$s_{ij} = a(v_j, v_i)$$

$$F_n = \{f_i\}_{i=1}^{N_n}$$

$$f_i = l(v_i)$$

$$X_n = \{U_i\}_{i=1}^{N_n}$$

Galerkin's method defines the following system of linear algebraic equations in matrix form:

$$K_n \cdot X_n = F_n$$

Which can be solved with the usual classical numerical methods.

It can be shown that for elliptic equations the Galerkin method converges:

$$\lim_{n \to -\infty} \|u - u_n\|_{V} = 0$$

Furthermore, by Cea's lemma, Galerkin's method is strongly consistent, i.e.:

$$\forall v_h \in V_h \Rightarrow a(u - u_h, v_h) = 0$$

For hyperbolic equations it is necessary to refer to the forward Euler scheme, also called upwind to the backward Euler scheme or to higher order schemes such as those of Lax-Friedrichs and Lax-Wendroff.
For example for a one-dimensional wave equation:

$$\frac{\partial u}{\partial t} + a \frac{\partial u}{\partial x} = 0$$

The discretization according to the forward Euler scheme is convergent if this condition holds:

$$c = \left| \frac{a \Delta t}{\Delta x} \right| \leq 1$$

This is called the Courant-Friedrichs-Lewy (CFL) condition.
As can be seen, this condition imposes a limit on the relationship between temporal and spatial discretization.
The parameter a usually has size and speed meaning.
At the n-dimensional level the condition transforms like this:

$$C = \Delta t \sum_{i=1}^{n} \frac{u_{x_i}}{\Delta x_i} \leq C_{max}$$

However, this condition is only necessary and not sufficient for convergence.
As far as the search for sufficient conditions for the convergence of hyperbolic equations is concerned, even more stringent conditions are needed, such as limitations on the diffusion coefficients, also known as numerical diffusion (an example is the limitation of the Peclet number for fluid-dynamic hyperbolic equations).

Also for partial differential equations, the leapfrog scheme can be used which, unlike the forward Euler scheme, is a second-order method that can be used for equations of the form:

$$\ddot{x} = F(x)$$

And the discretizations are given by:

$$x_i = x_{i-1} + v_{i-\frac{1}{2}}\Delta t$$

$$a_i = F(x_i)$$

$$v_{i+\frac{1}{2}} = v_{i-\frac{1}{2}} + a_i\Delta t$$

In this scheme the time discretization must be constant to maintain the convergence of the solution.

Exercises

Exercise 1

Let's approximate the integral:

$$\int_{\frac{1}{2}}^{\frac{5}{2}} -100\frac{(x-1)^2}{x}dx$$

Using the interpolation formulas on 2,3 and 5 points.

The exact integral is given by:

$$\int_{\frac{1}{2}}^{\frac{5}{2}} -100\frac{(x-1)^2}{x}dx - 100\left[\frac{x^2}{2} - 2x + \ln(x)\right]_{\frac{1}{2}}^{\frac{5}{2}} = 100 - 100\ln(5) \approx -60.9438.$$

The 2-point formula is:

$$S_1 = \frac{b-a}{2}(f(a) + f(b)) = \frac{2}{2}\left(-100\frac{(-0.5)^2}{0.5} - 100\frac{(1.5)^2}{2.5}\right) = -140.$$

The 3-point formula is:

$$S_2 = \frac{b-a}{6}(f(a) + 4f((a+b)/2) + f(b)) =$$

$$\frac{2}{6}\left(-100\frac{(-0.5)^2}{0.5} - 400\frac{(0.5)^2}{1.5} - 100\frac{(1.5)^2}{2.5}\right) = -\frac{620}{9} \approx -68.8889.$$

The 5-point formula is:

$$S_4 = \int_{\frac{1}{2}}^{\frac{5}{2}} p_4(x)dx =$$

$$\frac{1}{2}\int_0^4 p_4(t)dt = \frac{1}{2}\int_0^4 -\frac{5}{3}t^4 + \frac{55}{3}t^3 - \frac{230}{3}t^2 + 110t - 50dt =$$

$$\frac{1}{2}\left[-\frac{1}{3}t^5 + \frac{55}{12}t^4 - \frac{230}{9}t^3 + 55t^2 - 50t\right]_0^4 = -\frac{562}{9} \approx -62.4444.$$

Exercise 2

It approximates:

$$\int_{-5}^5 \frac{1}{1+x^2}dx$$

Using the simple quadrature formulas on 6 and 21 points.

The exact integral is:

$$\int_{-5}^5 \frac{(1}{1+x^2}dx = [\arctan(x)]_{-5}^5 = 2\arctan(5) \approx 2.7468.$$

The 6-point formula is:

$$S_5 = \int_{-5}^{5} \sum_{i=0}^{5} a_i x^i dx = \left[\sum_{i=0}^{5} a_i \frac{x^{i+1}}{i+1} \right]_{-5}^{5} = 2 \left[a_4 \frac{5^5}{5} + a_2 \frac{5^3}{3} + a_0 5 \right] \approx 2.3076,$$

The 21-point formula is:

$$S_{20} = \int_{-5}^{5} \sum_{i=0}^{20} a_i x^i dx = \left[\sum_{i=0}^{20} a_i \frac{x^{i+1}}{i+1} \right]_{-5}^{5} = \sum_{i=0}^{20} \frac{a_i}{i+1} \left[5^{i+1} - (-5)^{i+1} \right] =$$

$$2 \sum_{k=0}^{10} \frac{a_{2k}}{2k+1} 5^{2k+1} = 10 \sum_{k=0}^{10} \frac{a_{2k}}{2k+1} 25^k \approx -26.8496,$$

Exercise 3

Data:

$$f = \sin(\pi x) + 2 \cos(\pi x)$$

$$\int_{0.5}^{1.5} f(x) dx.$$

Estimate into how many subintervals to divide the given interval so that the remainders of the trapezium formula and the Cavalieri-Simpson formula are less than 0.01.

By the trapezium formula, the remainder has the form:

$$R_1^{(N)} = \frac{f^{(s)}(\xi)}{s!} \gamma_1 h^{s+1} N,$$

Where is it:

$$\begin{cases} s = n + 1 = 2, \\ h = \frac{1.5 - 0.5}{N} = \frac{1}{N}, \\ \gamma_1 = \int_0^1 t(t-1) dt = -\frac{1}{6}. \end{cases}$$

Given that:

$$f'(x) = \pi(\cos(\pi x) - 2\sin(\pi x)) \qquad e$$
$$f^{(2)}(x) = \pi^2(-\sin(\pi x) - 2\cos(\pi x)) = -\pi^2 f(x).$$

Substituting, we get:

$$R_1^{(N)} = \frac{\pi^2}{12N^2} f(\xi).$$

And then:

$$\left| R_1^{(N)} \right| = \frac{\pi^2}{12N^2} |\sin(\pi x) + 2\cos(\pi x)| \leq \frac{\pi^2}{12N^2} |\sin(\pi x)| + 2|\cos(\pi x)| \leq \frac{3\pi^2}{12N^2}.$$

The smallest value of N is 16.
By the Cavalieri-Simpson formula we have:

$$R_2^{(N)} = \frac{f^{(s)}(\xi)}{s!} \gamma_2 h^{s+1} N.$$

$$\begin{cases} s = n + 2 = 4, \\ h = \frac{1.5 - 0.5}{2N} = \frac{1}{2N}, \\ \gamma_2 = \int_0^2 t^2(t-1)(t-2)dt = -\frac{4}{15}. \end{cases}$$

Given that:

$$f^{(3)}(x) = -\pi^2 f'(x) \qquad e$$
$$f^{(4)}(x) = -\pi^2 f^{(2)} = \pi^4 f(x),$$

You get:

$$R_2^{(N)} = -\frac{\pi^4}{2880 N^4} f(\xi),$$

And then:

$$\left| R_2^{(N)} \right| = \frac{\pi^4}{2880N^4} \left| \sin(\pi x) + 2\cos(\pi x) \right| \le$$

$$\frac{\pi^4}{2880N^4} \left| \sin(\pi x) \right| + 2 \left| \cos(\pi x) \right| \le \frac{3\pi^4}{2880N^4}.$$

The minimum value of N is 2.

Exercise 4

Approximate the solution of the Cauchy problem with the Euler method:

$$\begin{cases} y'(x) & = & y(x) - x^2 + 2x \\ y(0) & = & 1 \end{cases}$$

In 0, 0.8, 1.6, 2.4, 3.2 and 4 as the step h varies.

It is a matter of constructing a sequence:

$$y_{i+1} = y_i + h f(x_i, y_i);$$

I our case:

$$y_{i+1} = y_i + h y_i + h(2x_i - x_i^2) = (1+h)y_i - h x_i(x_i - 2) \quad e \quad y_0 = 1.$$

Numerically we obtain the following table:

x	0	0.8	1.6	2.4	3.2	4.0
h=0.8	1	1.800	4.008	7.726	13.139	20.579
h=0.4	1	2.216	5.264	10.677	19.494	33.755
h=0.16	1	2.564	6.425	13.703	26.747	50.494
vero	1	2.865	7.513	16.783	34.772	70.598

Exercise 5

Given the Cauchy problem:

$$\begin{cases} y'(x) &= 2y(x) - 6x + 3 \\ y(0) &= 1 \end{cases}$$

Approximate the solution in the interval [0,3] using Runge-Kutta methods with s=1,2,3 and step h equal to 1/3.

For s=1 we have:

$$\begin{aligned} y_{i+1} = y_i + hf(x_i, y_i) &= y_i + h(2y_i - 6x_i + 3) \\ &= (1 + 2h)y_i - 6hx_i + 3h. \end{aligned}$$

Therefore:

$$y_{i+1} = \frac{5}{3}y_i - 2x_i + 1.$$

For s=2 we have:

$$y_{i+1} = y_i + \frac{h}{2}(k_1 + k_2),$$

$$\begin{aligned} k_1 &= f(x_i, y_i) = 2y_i - 6x_i + 3 \\ k_2 &= f(x_i + h, y_i + hk_1) = 2(y_i + hk_1) - 6(x_i + h) + 3 \\ k_1 + k_2 &= (1 + 2h)k_1 + 2y_i - 6x_i + 3 - 6h = 2(1 + h)k_1 - 6h. \end{aligned}$$

You get:

$$y_{i+1} = y_i + h(1 + h)k_1 - 3h^2 = (1 + 2h + 2h^2)y_i - 6x_i h(h + 1) + 3h$$

From which:

$$y_{i+1} = \frac{17}{9}y_i - \frac{8}{3}x_i + 1.$$

For s=3:

$$y_{i+1} = y_i + \frac{h}{4}(k_1 + 3k_3),$$

$$
\begin{aligned}
k_1 &= f(x_i, y_i) = 2y_i - 6x_i + 3 \\
k_2 &= f(x_i + h/3, y_i + hk_1/3) = 2(y_i + hk_1/3) - 6(x_i + h/3) + 3 \\
&= (1 + 2h/3)k_1 - 2h \\
k_3 &= f(x_i + 2h/3, y_i + 2hk_2/3) = 2(y_i + 2hk_2/3) - 6(x_i + 2h/3) + 3 \\
&= k_1 + 4hk_2/3 - 4h.
\end{aligned}
$$

And then:

$$h(k_1 + 3k_3)/4 = h(1 + h + 2h^2/3)k_1 - 2h^3 - 3h^2$$
$$= (1 + h + 2h^2/3)(2y_i - 6x_i) + 3h$$

From which:

$$
\begin{aligned}
y_{i+1} &= y_i + h(1 + h + 2h^2/3)(2y_i - 6x_i) + 3h \\
y_{i+1} &= y_i(1 + 2h + 2h^2 + 4h^3/3) - 6x_i(h + h^2 + 2h^3/3) + 3h
\end{aligned}
$$

Definitely:

$$y_{i+1} = \frac{157}{81}y_i - \frac{76}{27}x_i + 1.$$

Exercise 6

Given the nonlinear boundary problem:

$$
\begin{cases}
y'' = \dfrac{1}{8}(32 + 2x^3 - yy'), & 1 \le x \le 3, \\
y(1) = 17, \qquad y(3) = \dfrac{43}{3}.
\end{cases}
$$

Apply the nonlinear finite difference method with pitch h=0.1 and nodes:

1211

$$x_i = 1.0 + ih, \quad i = 0, 1, \ldots, 20$$

We get the following nonlinear system:

$$
\begin{cases}
2y_1 - y_2 + h^2 \dfrac{1}{8}\left(32 + 2x_1^3 - y_1\dfrac{y_2 - \alpha}{2h}\right) - \alpha = 0, \\[2ex]
-y_1 + 2y_2 - y_3 + h^2 \dfrac{1}{8}\left(32 + 2x_2^3 - y_2\dfrac{y_3 - y_1}{2h}\right) = 0, \\[2ex]
\cdots\cdots\cdots\cdots\cdots\cdots\cdots\cdots\cdots\cdots\cdots\cdots\cdots\cdots\cdots\cdots\cdots\cdots \\[2ex]
-y_{N-2} + 2y_{N-1} - y_N + h^2 \dfrac{1}{8}\left(32 + 2x_{N-1}^3 - y_{N-1}\dfrac{y_N - y_{N-2}}{2h}\right) = 0, \\[2ex]
-y_{N-1} + 2y_N + h^2 \dfrac{1}{8}\left(32 + 2x_N^3 - y_N\dfrac{\beta - y_{N-1}}{2h}\right) - \beta = 0,
\end{cases}
$$

The Jacobian matrix is:

$$
[J(y_1, \ldots, y_n)]_{ij} =
\begin{cases}
-1 - \dfrac{h}{2}\dfrac{y_i}{8}, & i = j-1, j = 2, \ldots, N, \\[2ex]
2 - \dfrac{h}{2}\dfrac{y_{i+1} - y_{i-1}}{8}, & i = j, j = 1, \ldots, N, \\[2ex]
-1 + \dfrac{h}{2}\dfrac{y_i}{8}, & i = j+1, j = 1, \ldots, N-1.
\end{cases}
$$

By Richardson extrapolation we get:

$$y_i^{E_1} = \frac{4y_i^{(h/2)} - y_i^{(h)}}{3}, \quad i = 1, \ldots, N,$$

$$y_i^{E_2} = \frac{4y_i^{(h/4)} - y_i^{(h/2)}}{3}, \quad i = 1, \ldots, N,$$

$$y_i^{E_3} = \frac{16y_i^{E_2} - y_i^{E_1}}{15}, \quad i = 1, \ldots, N.$$

Exercise 7

Given the boundary problem:

$$\begin{cases} y'' = \dfrac{2}{x}y' - \dfrac{2}{x^2}y + \sin(\log x), & 1 \le x \le 2, \\[2mm] y(1) = 1, \qquad y(2) = 2, \end{cases}$$

Whose exact solution is:

$$y(x) = \frac{x}{2}(4-x) - x(1-x)\Big(\cos(\log 2) + \sin(\log 2)\Big) - \frac{x^2}{2}\Big(\cos(\log x) + \sin(\log x)\Big).$$

Approximate it with the finite difference method.

We get a tridiagonal system:

$$\begin{bmatrix}
2 - h^2\dfrac{2}{x_1^2} & -1 + \dfrac{h}{2}\dfrac{2}{x_1} & 0 & \cdots & \cdots & 0 \\[2mm]
-1 - \dfrac{h}{2}\dfrac{2}{x_2} & 2 - h^2\dfrac{2}{x_2^2} & -1 + \dfrac{h}{2}\dfrac{2}{x_2} & 0 & \cdots & 0 \\[2mm]
\cdots & \cdots & \cdots & \cdots & \cdots & \cdots \\[2mm]
0 & \cdots & \cdots & -1 - \dfrac{h}{2}\dfrac{2}{x_8} & 2 - h^2\dfrac{2}{x_8^2} & -1 + \dfrac{h}{2}\dfrac{2}{x_8} \\[2mm]
0 & \cdots & \cdots & 0 & -1 - \dfrac{h}{2}\dfrac{2}{x_9} & 2 - h^2\dfrac{2}{x_9^2}
\end{bmatrix} X =$$

$$\begin{bmatrix}
h^2\dfrac{\sin(\log x_1)}{x_1} + \left(1 + \dfrac{h}{2}\dfrac{2}{x_1}\right)\alpha \\[3mm]
h^2\dfrac{\sin(\log x_2)}{x_2} \\[3mm]
\vdots \\[3mm]
h^2\dfrac{\sin(\log x_8)}{x_8} \\[3mm]
h^2\dfrac{\sin(\log x_9)}{x_9} + \left(1 - \dfrac{h}{2}\dfrac{2}{x_9}\right)\beta
\end{bmatrix}$$

Exercise 8

Given the boundary problem:

$$\begin{cases} -y'' + \pi^2 y = 2\pi \sin(\pi x), & 0 \le x \le 1, \\ y(0) = y(1) = 0. \end{cases}$$

Approximate it with the Galerkin method with 10 equally spaced nodes of h=0.1

We can calculate the exact integrals:

$$Q_{1,i} = 100 \int_{0.1i}^{0.1i+0.1} (0.1i + 0.1 - x)(x - 0.1i)\pi^2 \, dx = \frac{\pi^2}{60},$$

$$Q_{2,i} = 100 \int_{0.1i-0.1}^{0.1i} (x - 0.1i + 0.1)^2 \pi^2 \, dx = \frac{\pi^2}{30},$$

$$Q_{3,i} = 100 \int_{0.1i}^{0.1i+0.1} (0.1i + 0.1 - x)^2 \pi^2 \, dx = \frac{\pi^2}{30},$$

$$Q_{4,i} = 100 \int_{0.1i-0.1}^{0.1i} dx = 10,$$

$$Q_{5,i} = 10 \int_{0.1i-0.1}^{0.1i} (x - 0.1i + 0.1)2\pi^2 \sin(\pi x) \, dx =$$

$$= -2\pi \cos(0.1\pi i) + 20[\sin(0.1\pi i) - \sin(0.1i - 0.1)\pi)],$$

$$Q_{6,i} = 10 \int_{0.1i}^{0.1i+0.1} (0.1i + 0.1 - x)2\pi^2 \sin(\pi x) \, dx =$$

$$= 2\pi \cos(0.1\pi i) - 20[\sin(0.1i + 0.1)\pi) - \sin(0.1\pi i)].$$

The elements of the Galerkin equivalent problem are given by:

$$a_{i,i} = 20 + \frac{\pi^2}{15}, \qquad\qquad i = 1, 2, \ldots, 9,$$

$$a_{i,i+1} = -10 + \frac{\pi^2}{60}, \qquad\qquad i = 1, 2, \ldots, 8,$$

$$a_{i,i-1} = -10 + \frac{\pi^2}{60}, \qquad\qquad i = 2, 3, \ldots, 9,$$

$$f_i = 40\sin(0.1\pi i)[1 - \cos(0.1\pi)], \quad i = 1, 2, \ldots, 9.$$

Which lead to a tridiagonal system.

Exercise 9

Prove that for elliptic partial differential equations, Galerkin's method is strongly consistent (Céa's lemma).

Given an elliptical problem, the Lax-Milgram lemma guarantees that the weak formulation has only one solution.
Galerkin's method consists in finding a function such that:

$$a(u_h, v) = F(v) \qquad \text{per ogni} \quad v \in V_h.$$

Where a is a coercive bilinear form, i.e.:

$$a(v, v) \geq \alpha \|v\|_V^2 \qquad \forall v \in V.$$

This function looks like this:

$$\Psi_h \in V_h \subset V \qquad \text{con} \quad \dim V_h = N_h < \infty.$$

From this it follows that even the exact solution satisfies the weak problem, i.e.:

$$\{a(u, v_h) - F(v_h)\} - \{a(u_h, v_h) - F(v_h)\} = a(u, v_h) - a(u_h, v) = 0$$

Being bilinear, we have:

$$a(u - \Psi_h, v_h) = 0 \qquad per\ ogni \quad v_h \in V_h.$$

That is the thesis of strong consistency.

THIRD PART: STATISTICS, ADVANCED ALGEBRA AND ADVANCED LOGIC

Third part

43

COMBINATORY CALCULATION

Combinatorial calculus is the branch of mathematics that studies the possible configurations for grouping the elements of a finite set.
To do this it is necessary to introduce some operations that we are now going to expose.

Factorial and binomial coefficient

We define the factorial operation of any positive integer as the multiplication of the first n positive integers less than or equal to that number.
The factorial symbol is given by an exclamation point following the number itself.
In formulas we have:

$$n! := \prod_{k=1}^{n} k$$

By definition 0!=1 and therefore the factorial operation is also computed recursively:

$$\forall n \geq 1 \in N \Rightarrow n! := n(n-1)!$$

The binomial coefficient between two integers (positive and negative) is given by:

$$\forall n, k \in Z \mid 0 \leq k \leq n \Rightarrow C(n,k) = \binom{n}{k} = \frac{n!}{k!(n-k)!}$$

The properties of the binomial coefficient are given by:

$$\binom{n}{0} = \binom{n}{n} = 1$$

$$\binom{n}{1} = \binom{n}{n-1} = n$$

$$\binom{n}{k} = \binom{n}{n-k}$$

$$\binom{n}{k} = \binom{n-1}{k} + \binom{n-1}{k-1}$$

$$2^n = \sum_{k=0}^{n} \binom{n}{k}$$

The penultimate property generalizes the construction of the binomial coefficients according to the Tartaglia triangle.

The last property is used instead to define the binomial theorem, also called Newton's formula or Newton's binomial or binomial expansion which expresses the expansion in the n-th power of any binomial:

$$(a+b)^n = \sum_{k=0}^{n} \binom{n}{k} a^{n-k} b^k$$

Arrangements, combinations and permutations

A simple permutation (or without repetitions) is an ordered sequence of the elements of a set in which each element is present once and only once. The number of simple permutations of a set composed of n elements is given by:

$$P_n = n!$$

If, on the other hand, the sequence contains elements that repeat themselves, we speak of permutations with repetitions.

Said k the number of times that a single element repeats itself and generalizing up to r elements, the number of permutations with repetitions is:

$$P_n^{k_1,k_2,\ldots,k_r} = \frac{n!}{k_1!k_2!\ldots k_r!}$$

This formula generalizes the previous one, in fact by setting all the coefficients k equal to one, we see that we fall back into the case of permutations without repetitions.
A permutation is a bijective function within the same starting set.

A simple arrangement (or without repetitions) is an ordered presentation of some elements of a given set in which there are no repetitions of the same element.
The number of elements present gives rise to the length of the arrangement.
The number of simple arrangements of length k in a set of n elements is given by:

$$D_{n,k} = \frac{n!}{(n-k)!}$$

If k coincides with n, the simple arrangements coincide with the simple permutations.
If repetitions can occur in the ordered presentation of the k elements, we speak of an arrangement with repetitions.
The number of repeating arrangements of k elements in a set of n elements is given by:

$$D'_{n,k} = n^k$$

A simple combination (or without repetitions) is a presentation of elements of a set in which there is no ordering and each element cannot be repeated.
The number of simple combinations of k elements in a set of n elements is given by:

$$C_{n,k} = \frac{D_{n,k}}{P_k} = \binom{n}{k}$$

If repetitions can occur in the presentation, this is called a combination with repetitions.
The number of such combinations of k elements in a set of n elements is as follows:

$$C'_{n,k} = \binom{n+k-1}{k} = \binom{n+k-1}{n-1}$$

With these results it is possible to calculate all the different situations that may arise in aggregating distinct elements into a given set.

Exercises

Exercise 1

Calculate the maximum number of vehicles that can be registered under the current number plate system.

The current plate numbering system is based on two letters, followed by three numbers and then two more letters.
The letters can be chosen among the 26 of the alphabet, the numbers are 0 a9 digits, therefore 10 digits.
For groups of letters, the possible combinations are given by arrangements with repetition, therefore:

$$D'_{n,k} = D'_{26,2} = 26^2 = 676$$

For numbers there are always arrangements with repetition:

$$D'_{n,k} = D'_{10,3} = 10^3 = 1000$$

The total number of vehicles that can be registered is therefore:

$$N = 676 \cdot 1000 \cdot 676 = 456'976'000$$

Exercise 2

Seven work colleagues go to lunch every working day. Everyone orders, every day, a different dish from the others and a different dish for each day. After how many days will they have used all the possible combinations?

It is a question of calculating the possibilities given by the simple permutations:

$$P_7 = 7! = 5'040$$

It will therefore take colleagues about 20 working years to exhaust all the combinations.

Exercise 3

In how many ways can 7 numbered envelopes be given to 7 people, if each of them receives an envelope?

These are simple permutations, so:

$$P_7 = 7! = 5'040$$

Exercise 4

In how many ways can 7 numbered envelopes be assigned to 7 people?

These are provisions with repetition:

$$7^7$$

That is 823'543.

Exercise 5

In how many ways can 7 identical envelopes be assigned to 7 people?

It is arrangement with simple:

$$\binom{13}{7}$$

That is 1'716.

Exercise 6

10 tennis players decide to play doubles. How many distinct pairs can be formed? Once the pairs are formed, how many separate games can be played?

It's all about combinations.
Then the number of distinct pairs is given by:

$$\binom{10}{2} = 45$$

While the number of matches:

$$\binom{5}{2} = 10$$

Exercise 7

In a deck of 40 cards, how many sets of 5 cards can you have? And how many sets of 5 cards can 4 aces have? And how many sets of 5 cards can 4 cards of the same value (poker) have?

The number of sets of 5 cards is given by:

$$\binom{40}{5}$$

That is 658,000.
Sets of 5 cards containing four aces are 36 (from 40-4).
If we extend the concept to cards of the same rank (which are 10) we get 360.

Exercise 8

10 copies of a book are distributed in 5 schools. In how many ways can books be distributed?

For each book to be assigned, a school is chosen and therefore combinations with repetition will be obtained:

$$\binom{14}{10}.$$

That is 1'001.

Exercise 9

An urn contains 20 white balls and 10 black balls.
By performing 5 draws without replacement, in how many cases do you get 3 white and 2 black balls?
And if instead there is reintegration?

Without reinsertion we have:

$$\binom{20}{3}\binom{10}{2}$$

The value of which is 51,300.
With reintegration:

$$\binom{22}{3}\binom{11}{2}$$

The value of which is 84'700.

Exercise 10

Three people draw 5, 4 and 3 cards from a deck of 40 cards respectively. What are the possible draws where no one has drawn spades?

We apply the multinomial coefficient to the 30 remaining cards (ie to those that are not spades).

$$\binom{30}{5}\binom{25}{4}\binom{21}{3} = \frac{30!}{5!4!3!(18)!}.$$

Exercise 11

13 cards are drawn from a deck of 52.
How many possible draws are there where all 13 cards have different ranks?

For each value from 1 to 13 (the cards drawn) we must consider the choice of one of the four cards but of a different suit therefore:

$$4^{13}$$

That is 67'108'864 cases.

Exercise 12

Out of 100 numbered tickets, what are the probabilitys of getting tickets with consecutive numbers, choosing 4 at random?

The number of ways in which the first of four consecutive values can be chosen is 97.

Exercise 13

Four people play four musical instruments.
If every person knows how to play every instrument, how many possible ways are there to distribute them?

These are permutations, i.e. 4!= 24 ways.

Exercise 14

Given 6 red, 4 yellow, 1 green and 1 blue bricks, how many ways can they be stacked in a column to form a tower?

Bricks of the same color cannot be identified from each other, so these are combinations with repetition:

$$\frac{12!}{6!\cdot 4!}.$$

That is 27,720 ways.

Exercise 15

How many words can be formed with 5 distinct letters?

These are permutations therefore 5!=120 words.

Exercise 16

In how many ways can 3 boys and 3 girls fit on a bench?

These are permutations: 6!= 720 ways.

Exercise 17

How many ways can 8 people sit in order on a bench?

These are permutations: 8!= 40'320 ways.

Exercise 18

There are 3 books on literature, 2 on computer science and 1 on mathematics.
In how many ways can books be arranged in a library?

Since there are no distinctions between the elements, these are permutations: 6!= 720 ways.

Exercise 19

A student has decided to sell 2 books of his choice: 6 on mathematics, 7 on science and 4 on economics.
How many choices are possible if the books sold have to deal with the same subject?

These are combinations with repetition:

$$\binom{17}{2}$$

That is 136 possible choices.

Exercise 20

From a group of 8 women and 6 men, 3 of each gender are chosen.
How many different choices can you make?

The possible choices are given by the product of the choices for each gender:

$$\binom{8}{3}\binom{6}{3}$$

That is 1,120 choices.

Exercise 21

12 people are divided into 3 groups of 5,4 and 3 people. How many possible divisions are there?
This is the multinomial coefficient:

$$\binom{12}{3;4;5}$$

That is 27,720 divisions.

Exercise 22

In how many ways can 8 professors be assigned to 4 distinct schools?

Therefore, these are provisions:

$$4^8$$

That is 65,536 different ways.

Exercise 23

You want to invest 20,000 euros in 4 different stocks.
Each investment must be a multiple of 1,000 euros, but each share has a minimum investment: the first 4,000 euros, the second 3,000 euros, the third and fourth 2,000 euros.
How many different investments are possible if you want to invest in every stock?

If one invests in each of the securities, at least 11,000 euros are committed to the global investment.
The remaining 9,000 are distributed, in units of 1,000, over the four titles.
This is equivalent to choosing 9 out of 4 elements with repetition and no order, i.e.:

$$\binom{12}{9}$$

There are therefore 220 possible investments.

44

ELEMENTARY STATISTICS

Probability

To pass from combinatorics to probabilistic calculus, it is necessary to introduce the concept of probability.

A first definition of the probability of an event can be expressed as the ratio between the number of cases favorable to the event and the number of possible cases, having assumed the equiprobability of all possible cases. The number of possible cases is given precisely by combinatorics.

Let us denote by Ω the set of possible cases and P(A) the probability of event A.

The following rules apply:

$$P(A) \in R : 0 \leq P(A) \leq 1$$
$$P(A) = 0 \Leftrightarrow A \equiv \{0\}$$
$$P(A) = 1 \Leftrightarrow A \equiv \{\Omega\}$$
$$P(A) = 1 - P(\overline{A})$$
$$A \subseteq B \Rightarrow P(A) \leq P(B)$$
$$A \cap B = \{0\} \Rightarrow P(A \cup B) = P(A) + P(B)$$

Which state that the probability is a real number between zero and one and is worth zero only if A is the impossible event and one only if A is equal to the certain event (ie coinciding with the number of possible cases).

The fourth property takes into account the complementarity of an event and its opposite (and derives directly from the principle of the excluded middle), the fifth property explains the concepts of inclusion and increase, while the last property states that the probability of disjoint events is given by the sum of the probabilities of the single events.

Conditional probability and Bayes' theorem

We define the conditional probability of an event A with respect to an event B, that probability for which A occurs, knowing already that B has occurred.
The conditional probability is denoted by:

$$P(A \mid B) = P_B(A) = \frac{P(A \cap B)}{P(B)}$$

Where the so-called joint probability appears in the numerator.
If two events are disjoint, their conditional probabilities are zero.
If two events are independent, the conditional probability is the same probability of the single event.
If event A implies B, then the conditional probability of B with respect to A equals the certain event.
In formulas:

$$A \cap B = \{0\} \Rightarrow P(A \mid B) = P(B \mid A) = 0$$
$$P(A \cap B) = P(A)P(B) \Rightarrow P(A \mid B) = P(A) \leftrightarrow P(B \mid A) = P(B)$$
$$A \subset B \Rightarrow P(B \mid A) = 1$$

Bayes' theorem follows directly from the definition of conditional probability:

$$P(A \mid B) = \frac{P(B \mid A)P(A)}{P(B)}$$

Statistics

Statistics is the part of mathematics that contains both combinatorics and probabilistic calculus and gives a broader explanation by connecting them with other concepts.
First of all, statistics gives a definition of the set Ω that is called the sample space and of the algebra valid in it (called sigma-algebra).
The closure properties of sigma-algebra with respect to the sample space dictate that the certain event is an event, the negation of an event is also an event, and any union of events is an event.

In formulas:

$$\Omega \in A$$
$$A \in A \Rightarrow \overline{A} \in A$$
$$\forall i \in N : A_i \in A \Rightarrow \bigcup_{i=1}^{x} A_i \in A$$

The second element of statistics is the measure of probability given by probabilistic calculation.

The third element is the definition of a random variable (also called random or stochastic) which can assume different values on the basis of some random or probabilistic phenomenon.

The last element is given by the construction of the probability distribution, ie the function that can be associated with the mode of variation of the random variable.

Statistical parameters

The arithmetic mean is the sum of the value of each item divided by the number of items.

The weighted arithmetic mean is the same sum, but each element is weighted by a coefficient which determines its "weight" (ie its importance compared to the others).

The geometric mean is the nth root of the products of the n elements.

The harmonic mean is the reciprocal of the arithmetic mean of the reciprocals.

The power average is a generalization of the averages just exposed.

In formulas:

$$M_a = \frac{1}{n}\sum_{i=1}^{n} x_i$$

$$M_{a,pes} = \frac{\sum_{i=1}^{n} x_i f_i}{\sum_{i=1}^{n} f_i}$$

$$M_g = \sqrt[n]{\prod_{i=1}^{n} x_i}$$

$$M_h = \frac{n}{\sum_{i=1}^{n} \frac{1}{x_i}}$$

$$M_p = \sqrt[p]{\frac{1}{n}\sum_{i=1}^{n} x_i^p}$$

The mode, on the other hand, is the value that appears the greatest number of times in the statistical distribution under consideration.

The median is the value assumed by the statistical distribution when the value of the random variable placed exactly in the middle of its definition set is examined.

Instead, to measure the precision of the statistical data, the standard deviation is taken into consideration, which is an index of dispersion of the statistic under examination.

The standard deviation is given by:

$$\sigma_x = \frac{1}{\sqrt{n}}\sqrt{\sum_{i=1}^{n}(x_i - M_a)^2}$$

The exponentiation of this quantity is called the variance:

$$\sigma_x^2 = \frac{1}{n}\sum_{i=1}^{n}(x_i - M_a)^2$$

The weighted means of the variance values are called weighted means. The weighted arithmetic mean is:

$$M_{a,pond} = \frac{\sum_{i=1}^{n} \frac{x_i}{\sigma_i^2}}{\sum_{i=1}^{n} \frac{1}{\sigma_i^2}}$$

Exercises

Exercise 1

An urn contains 12 balls: 4 black, 4 white and 4 red. Compute the probability that, in a draw without replacement, 2 balls of the same color and 1 ball for each of the other colors are drawn.

The number of possible cases for drawing 4 balls from an urn of 12 is given by:

$$C_{n,k} = C_{12,4} = \frac{12!}{4!8!} = 495$$

There are 3 favorable cases: either two black balls, one white and one red or two white balls, one black and one red or two red balls, one white and one black.
The cases are equally probable so the favorable cases are three times the probability of the single case.
The favorable cases are:

$$C = 3 \cdot C_{4,2} \cdot C_{4,1} \cdot C_{4,1} = 3 \cdot \frac{4!}{2!2!} \cdot \frac{4!}{3!} \cdot \frac{4!}{3!} = 3 \cdot 6 \cdot 4 \cdot 4 = 288$$

So the final probability is given by:

$$P(E) = \frac{288}{495} = 0,5818$$

Exercise 2

In the lottery game, calculate the probability that multiple numbers of 6 will be drawn in the first two draws.

The probability is conditioned by the fact that the first drawn is a number of 6, therefore:

$$P(E \cap A) = P(E) \cdot P(A|E)$$

Where E is the event that the first extract is a multiple of 6, while A is the event that the second extract is a multiple of 6.
Since the lottery numbers are equal to the first ninety natural numbers, the number of favorable cases is given by:
6,12,18,24,30,36,42,48,54,60,66,72,78,84,90
Therefore there are 15 favorable cases out of 90.
At the second draw there will be 14 favorable cases out of 89.

$$P(E \cap A) = P(E) \cdot P(A|E) = \frac{15}{90} \cdot \frac{14}{89} = 0,0262$$

Exercise 3

Given the following set of elements: (1,3,5,2,1,5,7,8,1,4), compute arithmetic mean, geometric mean, harmonic mean, mode, standard deviation, variance.

The arithmetic mean, geometric mean and harmonic mean are calculated as follows:

$$M_a = \frac{1+3+5+2+1+5+7+8+1+4}{10} = 3,7$$

$$M_g = \sqrt[10]{1 \cdot 3 \cdot 5 \cdot 2 \cdot 1 \cdot 5 \cdot 7 \cdot 8 \cdot 1 \cdot 4} = 2,835$$

$$M_k = \frac{10}{1+\frac{1}{3}+\frac{1}{5}+\frac{1}{2}+1+\frac{1}{5}+\frac{1}{7}+\frac{1}{8}+1+\frac{1}{4}} = 5,71$$

The mode is 1, while the standard deviation and variance are:

$$\sigma = \frac{1}{\sqrt{10}} \sqrt{58,1} = 2,41$$

$$\sigma^2 = 5,81$$

Exercise 4

From a deck of 40 cards, 3 are drawn. What is the probability that they have the same suit?

The given probability is the ratio between the favorable cases and the total ones, i.e.:

$$\frac{4 \cdot \binom{10}{3}}{\binom{40}{3}}$$

The favorable cases are given by 4 (the number of suits) and by the binomial coefficient to the numerator (the ways of choosing 3 cards from the 10 of the same suit).
There is a probability of 4.858%.

Exercise 5

Two dice are rolled. Saying E the event that the sum of the numbers drawn is odd, F the event that at least one of the two numbers drawn is 1 and G the event that the sum of the numbers drawn is 5, calculate the probability of the event EF, FG , E or F, EFG, E and F denied.

The EF event is given by:

$$EF = \{(1,2); (1,4); (1,6); (2,1); (4,1); (6,1)\}$$

Therefore:

$$P(EF) = \frac{\sharp \text{ casi favorevoli}}{\sharp \text{ casi possibili}} = \frac{6}{36} = \frac{1}{6}$$

For the other events we have:

$$P(E) = \tfrac{18}{36} = \tfrac{1}{2}, P(F) = \tfrac{11}{36} \implies P(E \vee F) = P(E) + P(F) - P(EF) = \tfrac{23}{36}.$$

$$FG = \{(1;4), (4;1)\} \implies P(FG) = \tfrac{2}{36} = \tfrac{1}{18}.$$

$$P(E\tilde{F}) = P(E) - P(EF) = \tfrac{1}{2} - \tfrac{1}{6} = \tfrac{1}{3}.$$

$$G \subset E \implies P(EFG) = P(FG) = \tfrac{1}{18}.$$

Exercise 6

From a pack of 52 cards, 5 are drawn. What is the probability that they have the same suit?

The probability is given by the number of favorable cases compared to the total:

$$\frac{4 \cdot \binom{13}{5}}{\binom{52}{5}}$$

The probability is 0.198%.

Exercise 7

From a deck of 40 cards, 10 are chosen in order. What is the probability that the tenth card is an Ace?

Denoting by k the number of axes chosen, the ways they can be chosen are:

$$\binom{4}{k} k!$$

Furthermore, the ways in which 10-k cards other than aces can be chosen are given by:

$$\binom{36}{10-k}(10-k)!$$

Finally we need to consider the ways in which k-1 aces are placed on 9 cards:

$$\binom{9}{k-1}$$

At this point the probability is given by the ratio between the favorable cases, added up for each k, and the total cases:

$$\frac{\sum_{k=1}^{4} \binom{4}{k} k! \binom{36}{10-k}(10-k)! \binom{9}{k-1}}{\binom{40}{10} 10!}.$$

Exercise 8

Place 8 rooks on a chessboard. What is the probability that each rook is in a separate row and column?

A chessboard has 64 squares.
The total cases are given by the combination between 64 and 64-8=56 remaining cells.
The favorable cases are instead given by 8!
So the probability is:

1239

$$\frac{8!}{\left(\begin{array}{c}64\\56\end{array}\right)}.$$

Exercise 9

Given an urn A containing 3 red and 3 black balls and an urn B containing 4 red and 6 black balls, draw one ball from each urn. What is the probability that the balls drawn have the same color?

Said:

$$E_r = \{\text{le palline estratte sono rosse}\}$$
$$E_n = \{\text{le palline estratte sono nere}\},$$
$$E = \{\text{le palline estratte hanno lo stesso colore}\} = E_r + E_n$$

We have:

$$P(E_r) = \frac{3}{6} \cdot \frac{4}{10} = \frac{1}{5}$$

$$P(E_n) = \frac{1}{2} \cdot \frac{6}{10} = \frac{3}{10}$$

$$P(E) = \frac{1}{2}$$

Exercise 10

Given an urn with 5 red, 6 white and 8 green balls. If 3 balls are drawn without replacement, what is the probability that they have the same color?

Said:

$$E_r = \{\text{le palline estratte sono rosse}\}$$
$$E_b = \{\text{le palline estratte sono bianche}\},$$
$$E_v = \{\text{le palline estratte sono verdi}\},$$

$E = \{\text{le palline estratte hanno lo stesso colore}\} =$

We have:

$$P(E_r) = \frac{\binom{5}{3}}{\binom{19}{3}} \quad P(E_b) = \frac{\binom{6}{3}}{\binom{19}{3}} \quad P(E_v) = \frac{\binom{8}{3}}{\binom{19}{3}} \implies P(E) = P(E_r)+P(E_b)+P(E_v)$$

Exercise 11

Given an urn with 3 red and 7 black balls, A and B take turns drawing a ball from the urn without replacement until one of them has drawn a red ball. What is the probability that A draws the first red ball?

Said:

$$E = \{\text{A estrae la prima pallina rossa}\}$$
$$F_n = \{\text{la prima pallina rossa estratta è la } n\text{-esima}\}, \text{ per } n = 1, 2, \ldots, 8$$

We have (A plays first):

$$E = F_1 + F_3 + F_5 + F_7.$$

Taking into account the order of extraction, we get:

$$P(F_n) = \frac{\binom{7}{n-1}(n-1)!\binom{3}{1}}{\binom{10}{n}n!}, \quad \forall n = 1, \ldots, 8$$

$$P(E) = \sum_{k=0}^{3} \frac{\binom{7}{2k}(2k)!\binom{3}{1}}{\binom{10}{2k+1}(2k+1)!}$$

Exercise 12

M boys and N girls are randomly lined up in a row. What is the probability that in the i-th position there is a girl?

The number of favorable cases is given by:

$$n \cdot (n + m - 1)!$$

The probability is therefore:

$$\frac{n \cdot (n + m - 1)!}{(n + m)!}.$$

Exercise 13

10 balls are distributed in 5 boxes. What is the probability that m balls end up in the first box?

The ways in which m balls can be chosen are:

$$\binom{m}{10}$$

The probability is therefore:

$$\frac{\binom{m}{10} 4^{10-m}}{5^{10}},$$

Exercise 14

What is the probability that, when throwing two dice, at least one six is rolled knowing that the faces are different?

Said:

$$E = \{\text{i dadi hanno valore diverso}\}$$
$$F = \{\text{è uscito almeno un } 6\}$$

We have:

$$P(E) = \tfrac{5}{6}$$
$$P(EF) = \tfrac{10}{36}$$

Therefore:

$$P(F|E) = \tfrac{P(EF)}{P(E)} = \tfrac{1}{3}.$$

Exercise 15

Given an urn with 8 white and 4 black balls, 4 are drawn and replaced. Consider the i-th event given by the fact that the i-th extraction is a white ball and denote by X the number of white balls extracted.
Calculate the probability of the event E1-E3 knowing that X=3.

From Bayes formula:

$$P(E_1 E_3 | X = 3) = \frac{P(X=3|E_1 E_3) P(E_1 E_3)}{P(X=3)}.$$

The events are all independent, i.e.:

$$P(E_i) = \tfrac{2}{3}$$
$$P(E_1 E_3) = P(E_1)P(E_3) = \tfrac{4}{9}$$
$$P(X = 3) = \binom{4}{3} \left(\tfrac{2}{3}\right)^3 \tfrac{1}{3} = \tfrac{32}{81}.$$
$$P(X = 3|E_1 E_3) = P(E_2 \tilde{E}_4) + P(\tilde{E}_2 E_4) = \tfrac{4}{9}$$

Applying Bayes we have:

$$P(E_1 E_3 | X = 3) = \tfrac{1}{2}.$$

Exercise 16

Given an urn A with 2 white and 4 red balls, an urn B with 8 white and 4 red, an urn C with 1 white and 3 red, draw a ball from each urn and indicate with X the number of white balls drawn.
What is the probability that the ball taken from urn A is white given that X=2?

Place:

$$E_A = \{\text{la pallina estratta da A è bianca}\}$$
$$E_B = \{\text{la pallina estratta da B è bianca}\}$$
$$E_C = \{\text{la pallina estratta da C è bianca}\}$$

We have:

$$X = E_A + E_B + E_C.$$

From Bayes formula:

$$P(E_A | X = 2) = \frac{P(X=2|E_A)P(E_A)}{P(X=2)}$$

Given that:

$$P(E_A) = \tfrac{1}{3}, \; P(E_B) = \tfrac{2}{3}, \; P(E_C) = \tfrac{1}{4}.$$

And since the events are independent, we get:

$$P(X = 2) = P(E_A E_B \tilde{E}_C) + P(E_A \tilde{E}_B E_C) + P(\tilde{E}_A E_B E_C) = \tfrac{37}{108},$$
$$P(X = 2|E_A) = P(E_B \tilde{E}_C) + P(\tilde{E}_B E_C) = \tfrac{7}{12}$$

Applying Bayes again:

$$P(E_A|X = 2) = \frac{21}{37}.$$

Exercise 17

Given 20 machines, choose 2. Knowing that 5 machines are faulty, calculate the probability that the first machine chosen is faulty.

Place:

$$E = \{\text{la prima macchina è difettosa}\}$$
$$F = \{\text{la seconda macchina è difettosa}\}$$

We have:

$$P(E) = \frac{5}{20} = \frac{1}{4}$$

Exercise 18

100 people book a flight with airlines A, B and C. 60 fly with A, 25 with B and 15 with C.
A has a delay probability of 0.15, B of 0.1 and C of 0.05.
What is the probability that a random passenger's flight is delayed?

Place:

$$E_A = \{\text{il passeggero scelto vola con A}\}$$
$$E_B = \{\text{il passeggero scelto vola con B}\}$$
$$E_C = \{\text{il passeggero scelto vola con C}\}$$
$$F = \{\text{il passeggero scelto è su un volo in ritardo}\}$$

We have:

$$P(E_A) = \tfrac{3}{5}, \quad P(E_B) = \tfrac{1}{4},$$

$$P(E_C) = \tfrac{3}{20}, \; P(F|E_A) = 0.15, \; P(F|E_B) = 0.1, \; P(F|E_c) = 0.05.$$

Given that:

$$E_A + E_B + E_C = 1,$$

You get:

$$P(F) = P(F|E_A)P(E_A) + P(F|E_B)P(E_B) + P(F|E_C)P(E_C) = \tfrac{49}{100}.$$

Exercise 19

Said X is the result of rolling a die, X cards are drawn from a deck of 52 cards with replacement. Saying AND the event that at least one ace is drawn in the X draws, calculate:

$$P(E|X = k), \text{ per } k \in \{1,\ldots,6\}.$$

With each choice there is a 1/13 probability of drawing an ace.
So we have:

$$P(E|X = k) = 1 - P(\bar{E}|X = k) = 1 - \left(\tfrac{12}{13}\right)^k,$$

Exercise 20

Given 80 pupils and 120 pupils, it is known that 32 pupils wear glasses and 60 pupils wear glasses.
If two students are chosen, what is the probability that the first wears glasses?

Said:

$E = \{$il primo studente scelto porta gli occhiali$\}$

$F = \{$il primo studente scelto è un'alunna$\}$

$M = \tilde{F} = \{$il primo studente scelto è un alunno$\}$

It is known that:

$$P(E|M) = 1/2, \; P(E|F) = 2/5,$$
$$P(F) = 2/5, \; P(M) = 3/5.$$

Applying Bayes we have:

$$P(E) = P(E|F)P(F) + P(E|M)P(M) = \tfrac{23}{50}.$$

Exercise 21

Draw 3 balls without replacement from an urn containing 4 white and 6 black balls.
Denote the event that the i-th ball drawn is white.
To calculate:

$$P(E_i), \text{ per } i = \{1, 2, 3\}.$$
$$P(E_2|E_1), \; P(E_1|E_2), \; P(E_3|E_2E_1), \; P(E_3|E_2).$$

The probability of the i-th event is given by:

$$P(E_i) = \frac{4 \cdot \binom{9}{2} 2!}{\binom{10}{3} 3!} = \tfrac{2}{5}$$

From this it follows that:

$$P(E_1 E_2) = \frac{\binom{4}{2} 8}{\binom{10}{3} 3!} = \tfrac{1}{15},$$

From Bayes:

$$P(E_2|E_1) = \frac{P(E_1E_2)}{P(E_1)} = \frac{1}{6},$$
$$P(E_3|E_2) = P(E_2|E_1) = \frac{1}{6}.$$

45

RANDOM VARIABLES AND PROBABILITY DISTRIBUTIONS

Random variables, distributions and properties

A random or random variable is a measurable function on a sample space in which a probability measure is defined.

This variable can have values in R, and therefore have one dimension, or have more dimensions and in this case we speak of multivariate random variables.

Each random variable X can be associated with a distribution or probability law which assigns to each subset of possible values of X the probability that the random variable takes on value in that subset and is defined as follows:

$$P_X(A) := P(X \in A) = v(X^{-1}(A))$$

Where the last relation is the probability measure defined on the sample space.

If the random variable is discrete then the discrete probability function is defined as follows:

$$p(x) = P(X = x)$$

While if it is continuous, the probability density function is given by:

$$P(X \in A) = \int_A p_X(x)dx$$

Where A is a subset of the sample space and the integral is intended according to Lebesgue.

For multivariate random variables the following extension for the probability density function holds:

$$P(X \in A) = \int_A p_{X_1 \ldots X_n}(x_1, \ldots, x_n)dx_1 \ldots dx_n$$

This is called the joint probability density function.
On the other hand, the probability density of a single component, called the marginal density, is defined as follows:

$$p_X(x) = \int_R p_{X,Y}(x, y)dy$$

In the case of multivariate discrete variables, the following definitions apply for joint and marginal probability functions:

$$p_X(x_1, \ldots, x_n) = P((X_1 = x_1) \cap \ldots \cap (X_n = x_n))$$

$$p_X(t) = P(X = t, Y \in R_1) = \sum_{y \in R_Y} P(X = t, Y = y)$$

Instead, it is called a distribution function, a non-decreasing function, continuous to the right and with the following properties:

$$\forall x \Rightarrow F(x) \geq 0$$

$$\lim_{x \to -\infty} F(x) = 1$$

$$\lim_{x \to -\infty} F(x) = 0$$

Such that one has that:

$$F(x) = P(X \leq x)$$

The relations between the distribution function and the probability function are given by the following formulas, respectively in the continuous and in the discrete case:

$$F(x) = \int_{-\infty}^{x} f(u)du$$

$$F(x) = \sum_{x_i \leq x} p(x_i)$$

The following probability function (continuous case and discrete case) is called conditional distribution:

$$f_Y(y \mid X = x) = \frac{f_{X,Y}(x, y)}{f_X(x)}$$

$$p_Y(Y \mid X = x) = P(Y = y \mid X = x) = \frac{P(X = x \cap Y = y)}{P(X = x)}$$

If two random variables are independent then the denominators of these relations are unitary.

The expected value of random variables is defined as follows in the discrete and continuous cases:

$$E[x] = \sum_{i=1}^{\infty} x_i p_i$$

$$E[x] = \int_{-\infty}^{+\infty} xf(x)dx$$

The expected value of a constant is the constant itself, furthermore the expected value is linear and the expected value of the sum of the independent random variables is equal to the sum of the expected values of the single random variables (this result, however, does not require the condition of independence as necessary).
Furthermore, the expected value is monotonic, i.e. if one random variable is greater than another, then its expected value will also be greater than that of the other.
The conditional expected value of a random variable is the expected value with respect to a conditional probability distribution and can be expressed as follows, respectively in the discrete and continuous cases:

$$E[x \mid Y = y] = \sum_{x} x \frac{P(X = x \wedge Y = y)}{P(Y = y)}$$

$$E[X \mid Z] = E[X \mid \sigma(Z)]$$

We define variance as the following quantity:

$$\sigma^2(x) = E\left[(x - E[x])^2\right] = E\left[x^2\right] - E\left[x\right]^2$$

The variance is never negative and is zero only when the variable assumes a value with probability equal to the certain event.
The variance has the following property:

$$\sigma^2(ax + b) = a^2 \sigma^2(x)$$

Furthermore, for two independent random variables:

$$\sigma^2(x + y) = \sigma^2(x) + \sigma^2(y) = \sigma^2(x - y)$$

The variance of discrete and continuous random variables is given by:

$$\sigma^2(x) = \sum_{y \in X} (y - E[x])^2 P(x = y)$$

$$\sigma^2(x) = \int_X (y - E[x])^2 f(y) dy$$

The measure of the independence of two random variables is given by the covariance:

$$\mathrm{cov}(X, Y) = E\left[(X - E[X])(Y - E[Y])\right]$$

Which can be expressed like this:

$$\mathrm{cov}(X, Y) = E[XY] - E[X]E[Y]$$

Two independent random variables always have zero covariance (if the covariance is zero, however, the variables can also be dependent).
The covariance has the following properties:

$$\mathrm{cov}(X, Y) = \mathrm{cov}(Y, X)$$
$$\mathrm{cov}(aX + b, Y) = a\,\mathrm{cov}(X, Y)$$
$$\mathrm{cov}(X + Y, Z) = \mathrm{cov}(X, Z) + \mathrm{cov}(Y, Z)$$

The variance is given by the covariance applied to the same random variable.

In general, the variance of the sum of two non-independent random variables is given by:

$$\sigma^2(x+y) = \sigma^2(x) + \sigma^2(y) + 2\sigma^2(x, y)$$

Where the covariance appears in the last term.

The law of total variance states that:

$$\sigma^2(x) = E\left[\sigma^2(x \mid y)\right] + \sigma^2(E[x \mid y])$$

From this law we can obtain a value for the conditional variance:

$$\sigma^2(x \mid y) = E\left[(x - E[x \mid y])^2 \mid y\right]$$

For multivariate random variables, a covariance matrix can be expressed as follows:

$$\sigma_{ij} = \frac{1}{n}\sum_{h=1}^{n}(x_{hi} - \mu_j)^2$$

Where the second term in the squaring is the mean. The values on the diagonal of this matrix, i.e. those where i=j, represent the variances.

We define the simple moment of origin m and order k of a random variable (discrete case and continuous case):

$$\mu_{m,k} = \sum_{i=1}^{n}(x_i - m)^k p_i$$

$$\mu_{m,k} = \int_{-\infty}^{+\infty}(x - m)^k p_X(x)dx$$

If the origin m is equal to the mean, this moment is called the central moment.

The following expression for the discrete and continuous cases is called the moment generating function:

$$g(t) = E\left[e^{tX}\right] = \sum_{i=1}^{n} p_i e^{tX_i}$$

$$g(t) = E\left[e^{tX}\right] = \int_{-\infty}^{\infty} e^{tx} f_X(x) dx$$

From this function we obtain the simple moments which are the derivatives of order k calculated at the point t=0.
Given n independent random variables and defining X as their sum, then it holds:

$$g(t; X) = \prod_{i=1}^{n} g(t, X_i)$$

The Pearson correlation index of two random variables is the ratio of their covariance to the product of the square roots of their variances:

$$\rho_{xy} = \frac{\sigma_{xy}}{\sigma_x \sigma_y}$$

It is valid that:

$$-1 \leq \rho_{xy} \leq 1$$

If this index is positive, the variables are said to be directly correlated; if it is negative, inversely correlated, if it is zero, uncorrelated.

Notable inequalities

In statistics, some fundamental inequalities hold.
Cebichev's inequality states that, given a random variable of known mean and variance, we have that:

$$\Pr\left(\left|X - \mu\right| \geq \lambda \cdot \sigma\right) \leq \frac{1}{\lambda^2}$$

Markov's inequality holds for non-negative random variables:

$$\Pr(X \geq \alpha) \leq \frac{E[x]}{\alpha}$$

Given n independent random variables, each of which is limited in the minimum and maximum values between two values and that S is the sum of these variables, the Hoeffding inequality holds (for t>0):

$$P(S - E[s] \geq t) \leq e^{-\frac{2t^2}{\sum (b_i - a_i)^2}}$$

Jensen's inequality states that, given a convex function, the following holds:

$$\varphi(E[X]) \leq E[\varphi(X)]$$

Convergence

The convergence of random variables has several meanings in statistics.
A sequence of random variables with a given distribution function is said to converge in distribution (or in law) to the random variable X with distribution function F if the following limit exists finitely, for every point where F is continuous:

$$\lim_{n \to \infty} F_n(x) = F(x)$$

The convergence in distribution is indicated as follows:

$$X_n \xrightarrow{d} X$$

For any continuous and bounded function the convergence in distribution is equivalent to:

$$\lim_{n \to \infty} E[g(X_n)] = E[g(X)]$$

A sequence of random variables converges in probability to the random variable X if:

$$\lim_{n \to \infty} P(|X_n - X| \ge \varepsilon) = 0$$

And it is indicated by:

$$X_n \overset{p}{\to} X$$

Convergence in probability implies convergence in distribution.
A sequence of random variables converges almost everywhere to the random variable X if:

$$P(\lim_{n \to \infty} X_n = X) = 1$$

And it is indicated by:

$$X_n \overset{q.o.}{\to} X$$

Convergence almost everywhere implies that in probability.
A sequence of random variables converges on the r-th mean to the random variable X if:

$$\lim_{n \to \infty} E\left[|X_n - X|^r\right] = 0$$

If r=1 it is said to converge on the mean, if r=2 on the quadratic mean. Convergence in the r-th mean with positive r implies convergence in probability and convergence almost everywhere (the latter up to subsequences).

Discrete distributions

The discrete uniform distribution is the distribution that gives the elements of a finite set the same probability of occurring.

Given a and b as the extremes of the progression of the n elements, we can write the probability density, the distribution function, the expected value, the variance and the moment generating function as:

$$\frac{1}{n}$$

$$\frac{i}{n}$$

$$\frac{a+b}{2}$$

$$\frac{n^2-1}{12}$$

$$\frac{1}{n}e^{at}\frac{1-e^{\frac{n}{n-1}(b-a)t}}{1-e^{\frac{1}{n-1}(b-a)t}}$$

The Bernoulli distribution is a distribution of a discrete random variable that can take on only two values p and q, where q=1-p and is denoted by B(p).
The density and the distribution function are given by:

$$P(0) = q \Leftrightarrow P(1) = p$$

The expected value is equal to p, the variance equal to the product of p and q.
The moment generating function is given by:

$$q + pe^t$$

The sum of n independent random variables each of which has the Bernoulli distribution gives rise to the binomial distribution.
The density function, the expected value, the variance and the moment generating function are:

$$P(k) = \binom{n}{k} p^k q^{n-k}$$

$$E[S_n] = np$$

$$\sigma^2(S_n) = npq$$

$$g(S_n, t) = (q + pe^t)^n$$

The generalization of the binomial distribution to the case of several variables is given by the multinomial distribution, whose density function is given by:

$$P(n_1, \ldots, n_s) = \frac{n!}{n_1! \ldots n_s!} p_1^{n_1} \ldots p_s^{n_s}$$

The covariance matrix is given by:

$$m_{i,i} = np_i(1 - p_i)$$

$$m_{i,j} = -np_i p_j$$

The discrete probability distribution that models the probability for the number of events that occur successively and independently in a given time interval, knowing that on average a given quantity occurs, is given by the Poisson distribution, whose density is:

$$P(n) = e^{-\lambda} \frac{\lambda^n}{n!}$$

Where n is a natural number.
The expected value, the variance and the moment generating function are given respectively by:

$$E[Y] = \sigma^2(Y) = \lambda$$

$$g(t, Y) = e^{\lambda(e^t - 1)}$$

A binomial distribution converges in law to a Poisson distribution.

Given two Poisson distributions each with a reference parameter, their sum follows a Poisson distribution having a reference parameter equal to the sum of the parameters of the single distributions.
Furthermore, the conditional distribution of this sum distribution is equal to the binomial distribution having parameter equal to the ratio between the parameters.

The discrete probability distribution over the natural numbers that follow a geometric progression is called the geometric distribution.
The density function is given by:

$$\Pr(Y = k) = (1-p)^k p$$

The distribution function, the expected value, the variance and the moment generating function are:

$$P(T \le k) = 1 - q^{k-1}$$

$$E[T] = \frac{1}{p}$$

$$\sigma^2(T) = \frac{q}{p^2}$$

$$g(T,t) = \frac{p}{1 - qe^t}$$

The geometric distribution of parameter q describes the number of failures preceding the first success in a Bernoulli distribution.
Furthermore, this distribution is devoid of memory, i.e.:

$$P(T = m + n \mid T > m) = P(T = n)$$

The hypergeometric distribution models the random variable that matters, for r distinct elements drawn equally probably from a set of cardinality n, those that are in a subset of cardinality h.
The probability of obtaining k elements is given by:

$$P(k) = \frac{\binom{h}{k}\binom{n-h}{r-k}}{\binom{n}{r}}$$

The expected value and the variance are given by:

$$E[N] = \frac{rh}{n}$$

$$\sigma^2(N) = \frac{r(n-r)h(n-h)}{n^2(n-1)}$$

The hypergeometric distribution with r=1 coincides with the Bernoulli distribution having as parameter the ratio between h and n.
For functions of several variables it is possible to generalize the hypergeometric distribution into a multivariate hypergeometric distribution.

We define a degenerate distribution as a discrete distribution in which the probability distribution is concentrated in a single value.
The density function and the distribution function are unitary in this value and zero in every other value.
The variance is always zero and the expected value is equal to the reference value.

The Pascal distribution describes the number of failures preceding the nth success in a Bernoulli distribution of parameter p.
The density function is given by:

$$P(k) = \binom{-n}{k} p^n (-q)^k$$

According to this expression, the Pascal distribution is also called negative binomial.
The expected value, the variance and the moment generating function are given by:

$$E[T_n] = \frac{nq}{p}$$

$$\sigma^2(T_N) = \frac{nq}{p^2}$$

$$g_{T_n}(t) = \left(\frac{p}{1 - qe^t} \right)^n$$

Pascal's distribution describes the sum of n independent random variables having identical geometric distribution of parameter q.

The Skellam distribution describes the difference of two independent random variables both having a Poisson distribution.
The density function is given by:

$$P(n) = e^{-(\lambda_1 + \lambda_2)} \left(\frac{\lambda_1}{\lambda_2} \right)^{\frac{n}{2}} I_{|n|}(2\sqrt{\lambda_1 \lambda_2})$$

Where I is the Bessel function of the first kind.
The expected value, the variance and the moment generating function are given by:

$$E[Y] = \lambda_1 - \lambda_2$$

$$\sigma^2(Y) = \lambda_1 + \lambda_2$$

$$g_Y(t) = e^{\lambda_1 e^t + \lambda_2 e^t - (\lambda_1 - \lambda_2)}$$

A Panjer distribution is a discrete distribution on the natural numbers defined by recursion:

$$P(n) = p_k$$

$$p_k = (a + \frac{b}{k}) p_{k-1}$$

Based on the values of a and b, one can have degenerate, binomial, Pascal, Poisson distributions or have no probability distribution at all.
In particular, if a+b=0 we have the degenerate distribution, if this sum is positive and a<0 we have the binomial one, if the sum is positive and a=0 we have the Poisson one, if the sum is positive and a>0 we have has that of Pascal, if the sum is negative there are no probability distributions.
The expected value and the variance are:

$$E[x] = \frac{a+b}{1-a}$$

$$\sigma^2(x) = \frac{a+b}{(1-a)^2}$$

The Benford distribution is given by:

$$P(n) = \log\left(\frac{n+1}{n}\right)$$

And it's important in number theory.

Continuous distributions

At the continuous level, the continuous uniform distribution generalizes the discrete uniform distribution to a continuous set in which the probability distribution is uniform.
The probability density, the expected value, the variance, the moment generating function are given by:

$$f(x) = \frac{1}{b-a}$$

$$E[X] = \frac{1}{2}$$

$$E[Y] = \frac{a+b}{2}$$

$$Var(X) = \frac{1}{12}$$

$$Var(Y) = \frac{(a-b)^2}{12}$$

$$g_X(t) = \frac{e^t - 1}{t}$$

$$g_Y(t) = \frac{e^{bt} - e^{at}}{bt - at}$$

The continuous distribution of paramount importance is the normal or Gaussian distribution, whose probability density is given by the Gaussian function:

$$f(x) = \frac{1}{\sqrt{2\pi\sigma^2}} e^{-\frac{(x-\mu)^2}{2\sigma^2}}$$

With this notation, the expected value, the variance and the moment generating function are given by:

$$E[x] = \mu$$

$$\sigma^2(x) = \sigma^2$$

$$M_X(x) = \exp\left(\mu x + \frac{\sigma^2 x^2}{2}\right)$$

The general notation of the normal distribution is as follows $N(\mu; \sigma^2)$.
The normal distribution is an even function with axis of symmetry given by x=E[x].
A particular case occurs when the mean is zero and the variance is unitary with the standard normal distribution N(0,1) whose probability density is given by:

$$f(x) = \frac{1}{\sqrt{2\pi}} e^{-\frac{x^2}{2}}$$

Having the following graph:

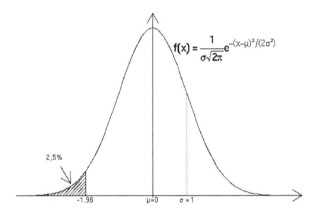

The sum of n independent normal random variables gives rise to another normal distribution whose expected value is a linear combination of the expected values of the single random variables and variance equal to the quadratic combination.

The central Lindeberg-Levy limit theorem states that, given a sequence of independent and identically distributed random variables having finite expected value and variance, the random variable:

$$S_n = \frac{\bar{x} - \mu}{\sigma} \sqrt{n}$$

It converges in distribution to N(0,1).
Basically, for n large enough, every continuous distribution that satisfies the above hypotheses converges to the normal one.
The strong law of large numbers states that, given a sequence of independent random variables having finite expected value and variance, the sample mean of that sequence almost certainly converges to the common mean.
The weak law of large numbers states that, given a sequence of independent random variables having the same expected value and the same variance, the sample mean converges in probability to the common mean.

The continuous exponential distribution has the following probability function:

$$f(x) = \lambda e^{-\lambda x}$$

The expected value, the variance and the moment generating function are given by:

$$E[x] = \frac{1}{\lambda}$$

$$\sigma^2(x) = \frac{1}{\lambda^2}$$

$$g_X(t) = \left(1 - \frac{t}{\lambda}\right)^{-1}$$

From the distribution function we can see that this distribution has no memory:

$$F(x) = P(X \le x) = 1 - e^{-\lambda x}$$

The exponential distribution generalizes the geometric discrete distribution to the continuous case.

The Cauchy distribution has the following probability function:

$$f_{(x_0, y_0)}(x) = \frac{1}{\pi} \frac{y_0^2}{(x - x_0)^2 + y_0^2}$$

This distribution has no moment generating function and neither expected value nor variance and therefore the central limit theorem does not apply to it.
The ratio of two independent random variables each with the standard normal distribution $N(0,1)$ follows the Cauchy distribution of parameters 0 and 1.

The gamma distribution has the following probability function:

$$f(x) = \frac{1}{\vartheta^k \Gamma(k)} x^{k-1} e^{-\frac{x}{\vartheta}} = \frac{\beta^\alpha}{\Gamma(\alpha)} x^{\alpha-1} e^{-\beta x}$$

Where is the Euler gamma function:

$$\Gamma(k) = \int_0^\infty t^{k-1} e^{-t} dt$$

The expected value and the variance are given by:

$$E[x] = k\vartheta$$
$$\sigma^2(x) = k\vartheta^2$$

The sum of n independent random variables each with gamma distribution of parameters ke theta has a gamma distribution equal to the sum of the ke theta parameters.
If k is a natural number, the gamma distribution assumes a simplified form called the Erlang distribution.
If k=1 we have the exponential distribution.

The beta distribution is defined on the unitary interval [0,1] and has a probability function given by:

$$f(x) = \frac{x^{\alpha-1}(1-x)^{\beta-1}}{B(\alpha, \beta)}$$

Where B is the Euler beta function:

$$B(\alpha, \beta) = \int_0^1 x^{\alpha-1}(1-x)^{\beta-1} dx$$

The expected value and the variance are:

$$E[x] = \frac{\alpha}{\alpha + \beta}$$

$$\sigma^2(x) = \frac{\alpha\beta}{(\alpha + \beta)^2(\alpha + \beta + 1)}$$

The sum of independent random variables having the standard normal distribution gives rise to the chi-squared probability distribution.
The number of independent random variables that are added together is called the degree of freedom and is denoted by the letter k.
The probability function is:

$$f_k(x) = \frac{x^{\frac{k}{2}-1} e^{-\frac{x}{2}}}{2^{\frac{k}{2}} \Gamma(\frac{k}{2})}$$

Where does Euler's gamma function appear?

It can be seen that the chi-squared distribution is a special case of the gamma distribution:

$$\Gamma\left(\frac{k}{2}, \frac{1}{2}\right) = \chi^2(k)$$

So the expected value and the variance are:

$$E[x] = k$$
$$\sigma^2(x^2) = 2k$$

Given n independent random variables and standard normals such that the following relationship holds:

$$\sum_{i=1}^{n} U_i^2 = Q_1 + ... + Q_K$$

And defined n as the sum of the ranks of the various Qs:

$$r_1 + \ldots + r_k = n$$

Cochran's theorem states that the various Q are independent and distributed as chi-squared variables each with respective r degrees of freedom.

The ratio between two random variables, the first with a normal distribution and the second with a chi-squared distribution, gives rise to another continuous distribution called Student's t.
This distribution is symmetric and has a probability function:

$$f(t) = \frac{\Gamma\left(\dfrac{n+1}{2}\right)}{\sqrt{n\pi}\,\Gamma\left(\dfrac{n}{2}\right)}\left(1 + \frac{t^2}{n}\right)^{-\frac{n+1}{2}}$$

The expected value is zero, the variance is given by (for n>2):

$$\sigma^2(T) = \frac{n}{n-2}$$

If n=1 this distribution corresponds to the Cauchy distribution of parameters 0 and 1.

The relationship between two random variables having chi-squared distributions is described by a continuous distribution called Fisher-Snedecor.
The probability density function is:

$$f(x) = \frac{1}{xB\left(\dfrac{m}{2},\dfrac{n}{2}\right)}\left(\frac{m^m n^n x^m}{(mx+n)^{m-n}}\right)^{\frac{1}{2}}$$

The expected value and the variance are:

$$n > 2 \Rightarrow E[F] = \frac{n}{n-2}$$

$$n > 4 \Rightarrow \sigma^2(x) = \frac{2n^2(m+n-2)}{m(n-2)^2(n-4)}$$

The Dirichlet distribution is a multinomial continuous probability distribution which has the following probability density function:

$$f(x_1, x_2, \ldots, x_k \mid \alpha_1, \alpha_2, \ldots, \alpha_k) = \frac{\Gamma(\alpha)}{\Gamma(\alpha_1)\Gamma(\alpha_2)\ldots\Gamma(\alpha_k)} x_1^{\alpha_1-1} x_2^{\alpha_2-1} \ldots x_k^{\alpha_k-1}$$

The expected value and the variance are:

$$E[X_i] = \frac{\alpha_i}{\alpha}$$

$$\sigma^2(X_i) = \frac{(\alpha - \alpha_i)\alpha_i}{\alpha^2(\alpha+1)}$$

If k=2 then each X is distributed as a beta function.

Exercises

Exercise 1

Two teams compete against each other by playing various matches. Whoever wins 4 games first wins.
Team A has a single match win probability of 3/5, Team B of 2/5.
Calculate the probability that team A wins in k games with k=4,5,6,7.

Given the independent events:

$E_k = \{$la squadra A vince la k-esima partita$\}$, con $k = 1, \ldots, 7$,

The number of wins of team A is given by:

$$X_k = E_1 + \ldots + E_k$$

Whose distribution is a binomial of parameters k and 3/5.

$$X_k \sim Bin(k, \tfrac{3}{5})$$

Defined:

$$F_k = \{\text{A vince in k partite}\}$$

We have:

$$F_k = \{X_k = 4\} \cdot E_k ,$$

And then:

$$\mathbf{P}(F_k) = \mathbf{P}(X_k = 4, E_k = 1) = \mathbf{P}(X_k = 4 | E_k = 1)\mathbf{P}(E_k) = \mathbf{P}(X_{k-1} = 3)\mathbf{P}(E_k)$$

$$= \binom{k-1}{3}\left(\frac{3}{5}\right)^4 \left(\frac{2}{5}\right)^{k-4} .$$

Exercise 2

A binary source generates 0s and 1s with probabilities of 0.4 and 0.6. Calculate the probability that 5 times 1 and 3 times 0 occur in an 8-digit sequence.
Called X the random number that counts how many times the digit 1 appears in a sequence n long, calculate the distribution and mean of X.

Given the independent events:

$$E_k = \{\text{la k-esima cifra è un 1}\}, \text{ con } k \in \mathbb{N}$$

The number of times 1 appears is given by:

$$X_n = E_1 + \ldots + E_n$$

Whose distribution is a binomial of parameters ne 3/5.

$$Bin(n, \tfrac{3}{5}).$$

The required probability will be given by:

$$P(X_8 = 5) = \binom{8}{5} \left(\frac{3}{5}\right)^5 \left(\frac{2}{5}\right)^3.$$

The distribution will be:

$$P(X_n = k) = \binom{n}{k} \left(\frac{3}{5}\right)^k \left(\frac{2}{5}\right)^{n-k}.$$

And the average:

$$P(X_n) = P(E_1) + \ldots + P(E_n) = \frac{3}{5} \cdot n$$

Exercise 3

In a quiz you have to choose the correct answer out of 4 dates. If there are 6 questions and indicating with X the number of wrong answers, calculate the probability of guessing 5 and the prediction of X.

Given the independent events:

$$E_k = \{\text{la k-esima risposta è esatta}\}, \text{ con } k = 1, \ldots, 6$$

The number of correct answers on 6 questions is given by:

$$X \equiv X_6 = E_1 + \ldots + E_6 .$$

Whose distribution is a binomial of parameters 6 and ¼.

$$Bin\left(6, \tfrac{1}{4}\right).$$

The probability of guessing 5 answers is:

$$\mathbf{P}(X_6 = 5) = \binom{6}{5} \frac{1}{4^5} \frac{3}{4} = \frac{18}{4^6}.$$

The average is:

$$\mathbf{P}(X) = \mathbf{P}(E_1) + \ldots + \mathbf{P}(E_6) = \tfrac{6}{4}.$$

Exercise 4

Roll a die 10 times and denote by X the number of times a number less than or equal to 2 is rolled. Calculate the distribution, mean and variance of X.
Calculate the probability of event X less than or equal to 4 conditional on knowledge of event X greater than or equal to 3.

The distribution is a binomial of parameters 10 and 1/3.

$$\mathbf{P}(X = k) = \binom{10}{k} \left(\frac{1}{3}\right)^k \left(\frac{2}{3}\right)^{10-k}.$$

The mean and the variance will be:

$$\mathbf{P}(X) = \mathbf{P}(E_1) + \ldots + \mathbf{P}(E_{10}) = \frac{10}{3}$$

$$\sigma^2(X) = \sigma^2(E_1) + \ldots + \sigma^2(E_{10}) = 10 \cdot \frac{4}{3} = \frac{40}{3}.$$

The conditional probability is given by:

$$P(X \le 4 | X \ge 3) = \frac{P(3 \le X \le 4)}{P(X \ge 3)},$$

With:

$$P(3 \le X \le 4) = \binom{10}{3} \left(\tfrac{1}{3}\right)^3 \left(\tfrac{2}{3}\right)^7 + \binom{10}{4} \left(\tfrac{1}{3}\right)^4 \left(\tfrac{2}{3}\right)^6$$

$$P(X \ge 3) = \sum_{k=3}^{10} \binom{10}{k} \left(\frac{1}{3}\right)^k \left(\frac{2}{3}\right)^{10-k}.$$

Exercise 5

A channel transmits sequences of 0s and 1s. Each digit is transmitted correctly with probability 0.8.
To reduce the error each digit is repeated 5 times and if more than half of the five digits are 0 then they are coded with a 0 (similarly with 1).
If we want to transmit a 6-digit number, determine the probability that a digit will be encoded incorrectly and determine the probability that the message will be encoded incorrectly.

The probability that a digit is encoded correctly is:

$$P(E_k) = \sum_{j=3}^{5} \binom{5}{j} (0.8)^j (0.2)^{5-j} \simeq 0.942.$$

Therefore the probability that the mode is wrong is 0.058.
The number of correctly encoded digits is given by a binomial distribution of parameters 6 and 0.942.
The message will probably be incorrect:

$$P(X_6 \le 5) = 1 - P(X_6 = 6) = 1 - (0.942)^6 \simeq 0.3.$$

Exercise 6

A student knows that if he is questioned by the assistant he has a probability of 0.8 of answering correctly, while if he is questioned by the professor this probability is 0.4.
Furthermore, the student will pass the exam only if he answers more than half of the questions correctly.
If the student thinks he is twice as likely to take the exam with the professor than the assistant, should he hope that he will be asked 3 or 5 questions?
Knowing that the student passed the exam by answering 3 questions correctly, what is the probability that he was questioned by the professor?

Be:

E_k = {lo studente risponde in modo corretto alla k-esima domanda }, con $k = 1, \ldots, 5$

F = {lo studente viene interrogato dal professore}

We have:

$$\mathbf{P}(E_k|F) = \tfrac{2}{5}$$
$$\mathbf{P}(E_k|\tilde{F}) = \tfrac{4}{5}.$$
$$\mathbf{P}(F) = 2\mathbf{P}(\tilde{F})$$
$$\mathbf{P}(F) + \mathbf{P}(\tilde{F}) = 1,$$
$$\mathbf{P}(F) = \tfrac{2}{3}$$
$$\mathbf{P}(\tilde{F}) = \tfrac{1}{3}.$$

The distribution on F will be a binomial with parameters ne 2/5, while on F negated with parameters ne 4/5.
If n=3 we will have:

$$\mathbf{P}(X_3 \geq 2) = \mathbf{P}(X_3 \geq 2|F)\mathbf{P}(F) + \mathbf{P}(X_3 \geq 2|\tilde{F})\mathbf{P}(\tilde{F}) =$$
$$\tfrac{2}{3}\left[3\left(\tfrac{2}{5}\right)^2 \cdot \tfrac{3}{5} + \left(\tfrac{2}{5}\right)^3\right] + \tfrac{1}{3}\left[3\left(\tfrac{4}{5}\right)^2 \cdot \tfrac{1}{5} + \left(\tfrac{4}{5}\right)^3\right] = 0.5\overline{3}$$

If n=5 we will have:

$$P(X_5 \geq 3) = P(X_5 \geq 3|F)P(F) + P(X_5 \geq 3|\tilde{F})P(\tilde{F}) =$$

$$\sum_{k=3}^{5} \binom{5}{k} \left[\frac{2}{3}\left(\frac{2}{5}\right)^k \cdot \left(\frac{3}{5}\right)^{5-k} + \frac{1}{3}\left(\frac{4}{5}\right)^k \cdot \left(\frac{1}{5}\right)^{5-k} \right] = 0.525653$$

So he has to hope for 3 questions.
From Bayes we know:

$$P(F|X_3 \geq 2) = \frac{P(X_3 \geq 2|F)P(F)}{P(X_3 \geq 2)},$$

But at this point the binomial will have as parameter not n but 3.
Therefore:

$$P(X_3 \geq 2|F) = 3 \left(\frac{2}{5}\right)^2 \frac{3}{5} + \left(\frac{2}{5}\right)^3 = 0,352$$

Exercise 7

Urn A contains 4 white and 6 black balls, B 8 white and 2 black, C 5 white and 5 black.
A ball is drawn from A. If it is white, then a ball is drawn from B. If it is black, a ball is drawn from C.
Calculate the probability that a white ball is drawn in the second draw.
Calculate the probability that a black ball is drawn in the second draw subject to the event that a white ball is drawn in the first.

are:

$E_A = \{$alla prima estrazione dall'urna A si estrae una pallina bianca$\}$
$E_B = \{$alla prima estrazione dall'urna B si estrae una pallina bianca$\}$
$E_C = \{$alla prima estrazione dall'urna C si estrae una pallina bianca$\}$

The probabilities of which are:

$$P(E_A) = \tfrac{2}{5}, \, P(E_B) = \tfrac{4}{5} \, eP(E_C) = \tfrac{1}{2}$$

Said F the event in question we have:

$$\mathbf{P}(F) = \mathbf{P}(F|E_A)\mathbf{P}(E_A)+\mathbf{P}(F|\tilde{E}_A)\mathbf{P}(\tilde{E}_A) = \mathbf{P}(E_B)\mathbf{P}(E_A)+\mathbf{P}(E_C)\mathbf{P}(\tilde{E}_A) = \frac{31}{50}.$$

The subordinate probability is instead given by:

$$\mathbf{P}(\tilde{F}|E_A) = \mathbf{P}(\tilde{E}_B) = \tfrac{1}{5}.$$

Exercise 8

An urn contains 8 white and 4 black balls.
Rolling a die, if an even number comes out, then two extractions from the urn are performed with reinsertion, while if an odd number comes out, two extractions are performed without reinsertion.
Calling X the random number that counts the number of white balls to extract, calculate the distribution, mean and variance of X.

Place:

$H = \{\text{dal lancio del dado esce un numero pari}\}$

$E_k = \{\text{alla k-esima estrazione si estrae una pallina bianca}\}$, con $k = 1.2$

We have:

$$\mathbf{P}(H) = \tfrac{1}{2}.$$

$$\mathbf{P}(E_k|H) = \mathbf{P}(E_k|\tilde{H}) = \tfrac{8}{12} = \tfrac{2}{3} \text{ per } k =$$

The distribution will be given by:

$$\mathbf{P}(X = k) = \mathbf{P}(X = k|H)\mathbf{P}(H) + \mathbf{P}(X = k|\tilde{H})\mathbf{P}(\tilde{H}) \quad \text{per } k = 0.1.2$$

In the case of extraction with reinsertion, the distribution is a binomial of parameters 2 and 2/3 and therefore:

$$\mathbf{P}(X = k|H) = \binom{2}{k}\left(\frac{2}{3}\right)^k\left(\frac{1}{3}\right)^{2-k}.$$

In the case of extraction without reinsertion, the distribution is a hypergeometric one

$$\mathbf{P}(X = k|\tilde{H}) = \frac{\binom{8}{k}\binom{4}{2-k}}{\binom{12}{2}}.$$

Knowing that:

$$\mathbf{P}(X = 0) = \frac{1}{2}\left(\frac{1}{3^2} + \frac{1}{11}\right) = \frac{10}{99}$$
$$\mathbf{P}(X = 1) = \frac{1}{2}\left(\frac{4}{3^2} + \frac{16}{33}\right) = \frac{46}{99}$$
$$\mathbf{P}(X = 2) = \frac{1}{2}\left(\frac{4}{3^2} + \frac{14}{33}\right) = \frac{43}{99}.$$

The mean, squared mean and variance are:

$$\mathbf{P}(X) = \sum_{k\in I(X)} k\mathbf{P}(X = k) = \frac{46}{99} + 2\frac{43}{99} = \frac{4}{3}$$

$$\mathbf{P}(X^2) = \sum_{k\in I(X)} k^2\mathbf{P}(X = k) = \frac{46}{99} + 4\frac{43}{99} = \frac{218}{99}$$

$$\sigma^2(X) = \mathbf{P}(X^2) - \mathbf{P}(X)^2 = \frac{218}{99} - \frac{16}{9} = \frac{14}{33}$$

Exercise 9

Urn A contains 14 white and 6 black balls, urn B 10 white and 10 black. A coin is tossed: if heads, two balls are drawn from urn A with replacement, if tails the same but from urn B.
Calculate the probability of drawing two white balls.

Said:

H = {dal lancio della moneta esce testa}
E_k = {alla k-esima estrazione si estrae una pallina bianca}, con $k = 1, 2$

We have:

$$\mathbf{P}(H) = \tfrac{1}{2},$$

$$\mathbf{P}(E_k|H) = \tfrac{7}{10}$$
$$\mathbf{P}(E_k|\tilde{H}) = \tfrac{1}{2} \text{ per } k = 1, 2.$$

The required probability is given by:

$$\mathbf{P}(E_1 E_2) = \mathbf{P}(E_1 E_2|H)\mathbf{P}(H) + \mathbf{P}(E_1 E_2|\tilde{H})\mathbf{P}(\tilde{H}) = \frac{1}{2}\left(\left(\frac{7}{10}\right)^2 + \left(\frac{1}{2}\right)^2\right) = \frac{37}{50}$$

Exercise 10

From a pack of 52 cards, 3 cards are chosen without repetition. Calling X the random number that counts the number of axes drawn, determine the distribution, mean and variance of X.

Said:

E_k = {alla k-esima scelta si estrae un asso}, con $k = 1, 2, 3$

We have:

$$\mathbf{P}(E_k) = \tfrac{1}{13}$$

The distribution is hypergeometric of parameters N=52, n=3 and H=4:

$$\mathbf{P}(X = k) = \frac{\binom{4}{k}\binom{48}{3-k}}{\binom{52}{3}},$$

The mean and variance are:

$$\mathbf{P}(X) = \mathbf{P}(E_1) + \mathbf{P}(E_2) + \mathbf{P}(E_3) = \frac{3}{13} \, .$$

$$\sigma^2(X) = \sum_{k=1}^{3} \sigma^2(E_k) + \sum_{j \neq k} \mathbf{cov}(E_j E_k) = \frac{3 \cdot 49 \cdot 4 \cdot 48}{(52)^2 \cdot 51} \, ,$$

Being:

$$\sigma^2(E_k) = \frac{1}{13} \cdot \frac{12}{13} \quad , \quad \mathbf{cov}(E_j E_k) = -\frac{4 \cdot 48}{(52)^2 \cdot 51} \, , \quad \forall j, k = 1, 2, 3 \, .$$

Exercise 11

Ten white balls are distributed in 2 boxes. For each ball, the probability of ending up in box 1 is 1/3. said Y the random number of white balls that are placed in the j-th box, we determine the distribution of Y for box 1.

Said:

$E_k = \{$la k-esima pallina è posta nella scatola 1$\}$, con $k = 1, \ldots, 10$

We have:

$$\mathbf{P}(E_k) = \tfrac{1}{3}.$$

We observe that:

$$Y_1 = E_1 + \ldots + E_{10} \quad , \quad Y_2 = \tilde{E}_1 + \ldots + \tilde{E}_{10}$$

And so the distributions will be:

$$Y_1 \sim Bin(10, \tfrac{1}{3})$$
$$Y_2 \sim Bin(10, \tfrac{2}{3})$$

Exercise 12

From an urn containing an identical number of black and white balls, extractions are performed with reinsertion.
Calculate the probability of getting a white ball within the fifth draw.
Knowing that, after 10 draws, no black ball has yet come out, calculate the probability of waiting at least three more draws before getting a black ball.

Place:

$$E_k = \{\text{la k-esima pallina estratta è bianca}\}, \text{con } k = 1, \ldots . 2n$$

We have:

$$\mathbf{P}(E_k) = \tfrac{1}{2}$$

And then:

$$X_k := E_1 + \ldots + E_k$$

It has a hypergeometric distribution.
The required probability is given by:

$$\mathbf{P}(X_5 \geq 1) = 1 - \mathbf{P}(X_5 = 0) = 1 - \frac{\binom{n}{5}}{\binom{2n}{5}}.$$

Where 2n is the total number of balls.
If after 10 extractions a black ball has not yet come out, the required probability is given by:

$$\mathbf{P}(X_{12} = 12|X_{10} = 10) = \frac{\mathbf{P}(X_{12} = 12)}{\mathbf{P}(X_{10} = 10)} = \frac{\binom{n}{12}\binom{2n}{10}}{\binom{2n}{12}\binom{n}{10}} = \frac{(n-10)(n-11)}{(2n-10)(2n-11)}.$$

Exercise 13

From an urn containing 8 black balls and 6 white balls, two draws are performed without replacement.
With each draw, you win 1 euro if the ball drawn is black and you lose 1 euro if it is white.
Let X be the random number that quantifies the budget in euro.
Determine the distribution of X, the mean and the variance.

Place:

$$E_k = \{\text{la k-esima pallina estratta è bianca}\}, \text{ con } k = 1, 2$$

We have:

$$\mathbf{P}(E_k) = \tfrac{3}{7}.$$

Called Y the random number that counts the number of white balls drawn in two draws we have:

$$Y := E_1 + E_2$$

Y has a hypergeometric distribution.
X has the probability distribution given by:

$$\mathbf{P}(X = -2) = \mathbf{P}(Y = 0) = \frac{\binom{8}{2}}{\binom{14}{2}}$$

$$\mathbf{P}(X = 0) = \mathbf{P}(Y = 1) = \frac{\binom{6}{1}\binom{8}{1}}{\binom{14}{2}}$$

$$\mathbf{P}(X = 2) = \mathbf{P}(Y = 2) = \frac{\binom{6}{2}}{\binom{14}{2}}$$

The mean, squared mean and variance are:

$$\mathbf{P}(X) = \sum_{k \in I(X)} k\mathbf{P}(X = k) = -2\mathbf{P}(X = -2) + 2\mathbf{P}(X = 2) = -\tfrac{2}{7},$$
$$\mathbf{P}(X^2) = \sum_{k \in I(X)} k^2\mathbf{P}(X = k) = 4\mathbf{P}(X = -2) + 4\mathbf{P}(X = 2) = \tfrac{13}{7},$$
$$\sigma^2(X) = \mathbf{P}(X^2) - \mathbf{P}(X)^2 = \tfrac{13}{7} - (-\tfrac{2}{7})^2.$$

Exercise 14

From an urn with 10 white and 15 black balls, extractions are performed with reinsertion until a black ball is drawn.
Calculate the probability that 20 draws are needed.

Place:

$E_k = \{$alla k-esima scelta si estrae una pallina nera$\}$, con $k \in \mathbb{N}$.

We have:

$$\mathbf{P}(E_k) = \tfrac{15}{25} = \tfrac{3}{5}.$$

Denoting the instant of first success as:

$$T = \inf\{k \; : \; E_k = 1\}$$

The distribution of T is a geometric of parameter 3/5, therefore:

$$\mathbf{P}(T = 20) = \left(\frac{2}{5}\right)^{19} \cdot \frac{3}{5}.$$

Exercise 15

A roulette made up of 37 numbers, you bet on a number between 1 and 12 coming up repeatedly.
Calculate the probability of losing the first 5 games.
Calculate the probability that the first win occurs on the sixth spin.

Place:

$E_k = \{$alla k-esima giocata esce un numero tra 1 e 12$\}$, con $k \in \mathbb{N}$.

We have:

$$\mathbf{P}(E_k) = \tfrac{12}{37}.$$

Denoting the instant of first success as:

$$T = \inf\{k \,:\, E_k = 1\}$$

The distribution of T is a geometric parameter 12/37, therefore the two required probabilities will be:

$$\mathbf{P}(T > 5) = \left(\frac{25}{37}\right)^5 .$$

$$\mathbf{P}(T = 5) = \left(\frac{25}{37}\right)^5 \frac{12}{37} .$$

Exercise 16

From an urn containing 5 red, 4 green and 6 yellow balls, 5 draws are performed without replacement. Given X the number of green balls drawn, calculate P(X), the variance of X and P(X+1)(X+1).
Do the same in case of reinsertion.

Place:

$E_k = \{$alla k-esima scelta si estrae un asso$\}$, con $k = 1, 2, 3.$

We have:

$$\mathbf{P}(E_k) = \tfrac{4}{15}.$$

X has a hypergeometric distribution of parameters N=15, n=5 and H=4, its mean and its variance are therefore::

$$\mathbf{P}(X) = n \cdot \frac{H}{N} = \frac{4}{3}$$

$$\sigma^2(X) = \frac{n(N-n)h(N-H)}{N^2(N-1)} = \frac{5 \cdot 10 \cdot 4 \cdot 11}{(15)^2 \cdot 14} = \frac{44}{63} .$$

Knowing that:

$$P(X^2) = \sigma^2(X) + P(X)^2 = \frac{44}{63} + \frac{16}{9} = \frac{52}{21},$$

It is obtained:

$$P((x+1)^2) = \frac{52}{21} + \frac{8}{3} + 1 = \frac{43}{7}.$$

In the case of re-entry, denoting the instant of first success as:

$$T = \inf\{k : E_k = 1\}$$

The distribution of T is a geometric of parameter 4/15.
Therefore:

$$P(T) = \frac{1}{p} = \frac{15}{4}, \qquad \sigma^2(T) = \frac{1-p}{p^2} = \frac{165}{16}.$$

Exercise 17

Given a variable X with geometric distribution of parameter p, choose p so that:
P(X=1)=2P(X=2).
We define Y as a random number independent of X with geometric destruction of parameter ½.
Let Z=X+Y.
Calculate p.
Calculate the probability P(X>P(X)).
Determine the distribution of Z.

The geometric distribution of parameter p is:

$$P(X = k) = (1-p)^{k-1}p.$$

The initial condition translates into:

$$p = 2(1 - p)p \implies p = 0, \frac{1}{2},$$

p=0 is a trivial case, so let's consider only p=1/2.
We have:

$$\mathbf{P}(X > \mathbf{P}(X)) = \mathbf{P}(X > 2) = \left(\frac{1}{2}\right)^2.$$

From the total probability formula, we have:

$$\mathbf{P}(Z = k) = \mathbf{P}(X = k - Y) = \sum_{j=1}^{\infty} \mathbf{P}(X = k - j|Y = j)\mathbf{P}(Y = j).$$

Recalling that X and Y are independent:

$$\mathbf{P}(Z = k) = \sum_{j=1}^{k-1} \mathbf{P}(X = k-j)\mathbf{P}(Y = j) = \sum_{j=1}^{k-1} \left(\frac{1}{2}\right)^{k-j} \left(\frac{1}{2}\right)^{j} = (k-1)\left(\frac{1}{2}\right)^k.$$

Exercise 18

The number of telephone calls arriving at a switchboard every 10 minutes is distributed as a Poissonian of parameter 2.
Calculate the probability that more than three calls arrive in a 10-minute period.

The required probability is simply:

$$\mathbf{P}(X > 3) = 1 - \mathbf{P}(X \leq 3) = 1 - \sum_{k=0}^{3} \frac{2^k}{k!}e^{-2} = 1 - e^{-2}(1+2+2+\frac{4}{3}) = 1 - \frac{19}{3}e^{-2}$$

Exercise 19

X and Y are two independent random numbers with Poisson distributions having different parameters.
Let Z=X+Y.
Calculate P(X=k | Z=n).

From the total probability formula, we have:

$$\mathbf{P}(Z = k) = \mathbf{P}(X = k - Y) = \sum_{j=1}^{\infty} \mathbf{P}(X = k - j | Y = j) \mathbf{P}(Y = j).$$

Recalling that X and Y are independent:

$$\mathbf{P}(Z = k) = \sum_{j=0}^{k} \mathbf{P}(X = k - j) \mathbf{P}(Y = j) = \sum_{j=0}^{k} \frac{\lambda^{k-j}}{(k-j)!} e^{-\lambda} \frac{\mu^j}{j!} e^{-\mu}.$$

Rearranging the terms:

$$\mathbf{P}(Z = k) = e^{-(\lambda+\mu)} \frac{1}{k!} \sum_{j=0}^{k} \frac{k!}{(k-j)!j!} \lambda^{k-j} \mu^j = e^{-(\lambda+\mu)} \frac{(\lambda+\mu)^k}{k!}.$$

So Z has Poisson distribution of parameter given by the sum of the parameters of X and Y.

Exercise 20

A die is rolled twice. Let X and Y be the results of the two tosses. Let Z=XY and U=XY.
Calculate the distributions of Z and U and whether they are independent.

The number of possible cases is 36. Z and U will be:

$P(Z = 1) = \frac{1}{36}$ (coppia $(1,1)$), $P(Z = 2) = \frac{2}{36}$ (coppie $(1,2),(2,1)$), $P(Z = 3) = \frac{2}{36}$, $P(Z = 4) = \frac{3}{36}$, $P(Z = 5) = \frac{2}{36}$, $P(Z = 6) = \frac{4}{36}$, $P(Z = 8) = \frac{2}{36}$.
$P(Z = 9) = \frac{1}{36}$, $P(Z = 10) = \frac{2}{36}$, $P(Z = 12) = \frac{4}{36}$, $P(Z = 15) = \frac{2}{36}$,
$P(Z = 16) = \frac{1}{36}$, $P(Z = 18) = \frac{2}{36}$, $P(Z = 20) = \frac{2}{36}$, $P(Z = 24) = \frac{2}{36}$,
$P(Z = 5) = \frac{1}{36}$, $P(Z = 30) = \frac{2}{36}$, $P(Z = 36) = \frac{1}{36}$.

$$P(U = -5) = P(U = 5) = \tfrac{1}{36}, \; P(U = -4) = P(U = 4) = \tfrac{2}{36},$$
$$P(U = -3) = P(U = 3) = \tfrac{3}{36}, \; P(U = -2) = P(U = 2) = \tfrac{4}{36},$$
$$P(U = -1) = P(U = 1) = \tfrac{5}{36}, \; P(U = 0) = \tfrac{6}{36}.$$

Independence occurs if:

$$\mathbf{P}(Z = z, U = u) = \mathbf{P}(Z = z)\mathbf{P}(U = u)$$

If we take z=1 eu=4 we see that

$$P(Z = 1, U = 5) \neq P(Z = 1)\mathbf{P}(U = 5)$$

And therefore Z and U are not independent.

Exercise 21

Urn A contains 10 white and 10 black balls, B 5 white and 15 black.
A coin is tossed, if heads then 3 draws are made without replacement from
A, otherwise 5 draws are made without replacement from B.
Calculate the probability that 2 white balls are drawn.

Place:

$E = \{$dal lancio della moneta esce testa$\}$,

$F = \{$vengono estratte esattamente 2 palline bianche$\}$,

$G = \{$viene estratta almeno 1 pallina nera$\}$.

We have:

$$\mathbf{P}(F|E) = \frac{\binom{10}{2} \cdot \binom{10}{1}}{\binom{20}{3}} = \frac{15}{38}.$$

$$\mathbf{P}(F|\tilde{E}) = \binom{5}{2} \cdot \left(\frac{5}{20}\right)^2 \cdot \left(\frac{15}{20}\right)^3 = 10 \cdot \frac{3^3}{4^5} = \frac{135}{512}.$$

$$P(E) = P(\check{E}) = \tfrac{1}{2}$$

And then:

$$P(F) = P(F|E)P(E) + P(F|\check{E})P(\check{E}) = \frac{1}{2}\left(\frac{15}{38} + \frac{135}{512}\right).$$

Exercise 22

Three draws are made from a deck of 40 cards.
Calculate the probability of drawing at least two figures in the cases of reintegration and without reintegration.

Place:

$$F_k = \{\text{vengono estratte k figure in 3 estrazioni}\}$$

We note that the required probability is given by:

$$P(F_2) + P(F_3).$$

We have, for the case without reinsertion:

$$P(F_k) = \frac{\binom{12}{k}\binom{28}{3-k}}{\binom{40}{3}}$$

While with reinstatement:

$$P(F_k) = \binom{3}{k}\left(\frac{3}{10}\right)^k\left(\frac{7}{10}\right)^{3-k}$$

Exercise 23

From a deck of 52 cards, extractions are performed with reinsertion.

Calculate the probability of drawing at least one ace in the first three draws.

Place:

$E_i = \{\text{all'}i\text{-esima estrazione viene estratto un asso}\}$, con $i = 1, 2, 3$,

We have:

$$\mathbf{P}(E_i) = \frac{4}{52} = \frac{1}{13} \quad , \quad \mathbf{P}(\tilde{E}_i) = \frac{12}{13}, \forall i = 1, 2, 3.$$

Noting that:

$$\tilde{F} = \tilde{E}_1 \tilde{E}_2 \tilde{E}_3$$

You get:

$$\mathbf{P}(F) = 1 - \mathbf{P}(\tilde{F}) = 1 - \mathbf{P}(E_1)^3 = 1 - \left(\frac{12}{13}\right)^3 .$$

Exercise 24

The pair of random numbers (X,Y) has the following joint distribution.

$$\mathbf{P}(X = -1, Y = -1) = \frac{1}{12} \quad \mathbf{P}(X = -1, Y = 1) = \frac{1}{6} \quad \mathbf{P}(X = -1, Y = 2) = \frac{1}{4}$$

$$\mathbf{P}(X = 2, Y = -1) = \frac{1}{12} \quad \mathbf{P}(X = 2, Y = 1) = \frac{1}{4} \quad \mathbf{P}(X = 2, Y = 2) = \frac{1}{6}$$

Find the marginal probability distribution of X and Y.
Calculate the mean and variance of X and of Y.
Let Z=X+Y, determine the probability distribution of Z.

We observe that:

$$I(X) = \{-1,2\} \ e \ I(Y) = \{-1,1,2\}.$$

We also recall the relation linking the joint to the marginals:

$$\mathbf{P}(X = k) = \sum_{i \in I(Y)} \mathbf{P}(X = k, Y = i)$$

So the marginal distributions are:

$$\mathbf{P}(X = -1) = \tfrac{1}{12} + \tfrac{1}{6} + \tfrac{1}{4} = \tfrac{1}{2} \quad , \quad \mathbf{P}(X = 2) = \tfrac{1}{12} + \tfrac{1}{4} + \tfrac{1}{6} = \tfrac{1}{2}$$
$$\mathbf{P}(Y = -1) = \tfrac{1}{12} + \tfrac{1}{12} = \tfrac{1}{6}, \ \mathbf{P}(Y = 1) = \tfrac{1}{6} + \tfrac{1}{4} = \tfrac{5}{12}, \ \mathbf{P}(Y = 2) = \tfrac{1}{4} + \tfrac{1}{6} = \tfrac{5}{12}.$$

The mean of X and Y are:

$$\mathbf{P}(X) = -1 \cdot \mathbf{P}(X = -1) + 2 \cdot \mathbf{P}(X = 2) = \tfrac{1}{2}$$
$$\mathbf{P}(Y) = -1 \cdot \mathbf{P}(Y = -1) + 1 \cdot \mathbf{P}(Y = 1) + 2\mathbf{P}(Y = 2) = \tfrac{13}{12}$$

For the variances we proceed as follows:

$$\mathbf{P}(X^2) = (-1)^2 \cdot \mathbf{P}(X = -1) + 2^2 \cdot \mathbf{P}(X = 1) = \tfrac{5}{2}$$
$$\sigma^2(X) = \mathbf{P}(X^2) - \mathbf{P}(X)^2 = \tfrac{9}{4}.$$
$$\mathbf{P}(Y^2) = (-1)^2 \cdot \mathbf{P}(Y = -1) + 1^2 \cdot \mathbf{P}(Y = 1) + 2^2\mathbf{P}(Y = 2) = \tfrac{9}{4}$$
$$\sigma^2(Y) = \mathbf{P}(Y^2) - \mathbf{P}(Y)^2 = \tfrac{155}{144}.$$

Passing to Z we have:

$$I(Z) = \{-2, 0, 1, 3, 4\}.$$

From the definition of probability distribution:

$$\mathbf{P}(Z = k) = \sum_{(i,j): \, i+j=k} \mathbf{P}(X = i, Y = j).$$

It is obtained:

$$\mathbf{P}(Z = -2) = \tfrac{1}{12}, \qquad \mathbf{P}(Z = 0) = \tfrac{1}{6},$$
$$\mathbf{P}(Z = 1) = \tfrac{1}{12} + \tfrac{1}{4} = \tfrac{1}{3}, \quad \mathbf{P}(Z = 3) = \tfrac{1}{4}, \quad \mathbf{P}(Z = 4) = \tfrac{1}{6}.$$

Exercise 25

By rolling two dice, calculate the probability that the sum of the results is a prime number.
Also calculate the probability that the product of the results equals the sum.

Given X the result of the first die roll and Y that of the second, the number of possible cases is 36, each of which are equally probable.
Said Z=X+Y we have:

$$\mathbf{P}(Z \in P) = \sum_{k \in P} \mathbf{P}(Z = p) \, .$$

Where P is the set of prime numbers ranging from 2 to 12:

$$P = \{2, 3, 5, 7, 11\}$$

We have that:

$$\mathbf{P}(Z = 2) = \tfrac{1}{36} \text{ (coppia } (1,1)), \quad \mathbf{P}(Z = 3) = \tfrac{2}{36} \text{ (coppie } (1,2), (2,1)),$$
$$\mathbf{P}(Z = 5) = \tfrac{4}{36}. \quad \mathbf{P}(Z = 7) = \tfrac{6}{36}, \quad \mathbf{P}(Z = 11) = \tfrac{2}{36}.$$

The product is equal to the sum only if 2 and 2 come out so the probability is 1/36.

Exercise 26

Eligibility for a service is awarded in a competition. It is assumed that each participant has probability p=1/3 of being eligible. At the end of the competition, 10 of the suitable candidates are assigned a job.
Suppose 15 people participate in the competition and X is the random number of participants who obtain eligibility but no job. Find the distribution, mean and variance of X.

Place:

$$E_k = \{\text{il k-esimo partecipante ottiene l'idoneità}\}, \text{ con } k = 1, 2, \dots, 15.$$

We denote by Y the eligible participants.
Y has a binomial distribution of parameters 15 and 1/3.
You will have:

$$X = \max\{0, Y - 10\}, \qquad \text{con } I(X) = \{0, 1, \ldots, 5\}.$$

So the distribution of X will be:

$$\mathbf{P}(X = 0) = \mathbf{P}(Y \leq 10) = \sum_{k=0}^{10} \binom{15}{k} \left(\frac{1}{3}\right)^k \left(\frac{2}{3}\right)^{15-k}$$
$$\mathbf{P}(X = 1) = \mathbf{P}(Y = 11) = \binom{15}{11} \left(\frac{1}{3}\right)^{11} \left(\frac{2}{3}\right)^4$$
$$\mathbf{P}(X = 2) = \mathbf{P}(Y = 12) = \binom{15}{12} \left(\frac{1}{3}\right)^{12} \left(\frac{2}{3}\right)^3$$
$$\vdots$$
$$\mathbf{P}(X = 5) = \mathbf{P}(Y = 15) = \binom{15}{15} \left(\frac{1}{3}\right)^{15}.$$

The mean, squared mean and variance are derived from their definitions:

$$\mathbf{P}(X) = \sum_{k \in I(X)} k \mathbf{P}(X = k) = \sum_{k=1}^{5} k \binom{15}{10+k} \left(\frac{1}{3}\right)^{10+k} \left(\frac{2}{3}\right)^{5-k}.$$

$$\mathbf{P}(X^2) = \sum_{k \in I(X)} k^2 \mathbf{P}(X = k) = \sum_{k=1}^{5} k^2 \binom{15}{10+k} \left(\frac{1}{3}\right)^{10+k} \left(\frac{2}{3}\right)^{5-k}.$$

$$\sigma^2(X) = \mathbf{P}(X^2) - \mathbf{P}(X)^2.$$

Exercise 27

Roll a die 5 times and let X be the number that counts the number of times the number 4 comes up. Determine the distribution, mean and variance of X.

Place;

$$E_k = \{\text{al k-esimo lancio esce } 4\}, \text{ con } k = 1, 2, \ldots, 5.$$

We have that X has a binomial distribution of parameters 5 and 1/6:

$$\mathbf{P}(X = k) = \binom{5}{k}\left(\frac{1}{6}\right)^{k}\left(\frac{5}{6}\right)^{5-k}, \quad \forall k \in I(X).$$

The mean and variance are:

$$\mathbf{P}(X) = np = \frac{5}{6}, \qquad \sigma^{2}(X) = np(1 - p) = \frac{25}{36}.$$

Exercise 28

Urn A contains two red and two white tokens, B two red and three white. One token is drawn from A and one from B.
Calling X the random number indicating the total number of red tokens drawn, calculate distributions, mean and variance of X.

Place:

$$E_A = \{\text{dall'urna } A \text{ viene estratto un gettone rosso }\}$$
$$E_B = \{\text{dall'urna } B \text{ viene estratto un gettone rosso }\}$$

We have:

$$\mathbf{P}(E_A) = \tfrac{1}{2},\ \mathbf{P}(E_B) = \tfrac{2}{5},$$
$$X = E_A + E_B.$$

The distribution of X will be:

$$\mathbf{P}(X = 0) = \mathbf{P}(\tilde{E}_A\tilde{E}_B) = \mathbf{P}(\tilde{E}_A)\mathbf{P}(\tilde{E}_B) = \tfrac{3}{10}$$
$$\mathbf{P}(X = 1) = \mathbf{P}(E_A\tilde{E}_B) + \mathbf{P}(\tilde{E}_A E_B) = \tfrac{1}{2}\tfrac{3}{5} + \tfrac{1}{2}\tfrac{2}{5} = \tfrac{1}{2}$$
$$\mathbf{P}(X = 2) = \mathbf{P}(E_A E_B) = \mathbf{P}(E_A)\mathbf{P}(E_B) = \tfrac{1}{5}$$

The mean, mean square, and variance of X are:

$$P(X) = P(E_A) + P(E_B) = \frac{1}{2} + \frac{2}{5} = \frac{9}{10}$$

$$P(X^2) = \sum_{k \in I(X)} k P(X = k) = \frac{1}{2} + \frac{4}{5} = \frac{13}{10}$$

$$\sigma^2(X) = P(X^2) - P(X)^2 = \frac{13}{10} - \frac{81}{100} = \frac{49}{100} \, .$$

Exercise 29

An urn contains 20 numbered balls. Four extractions are performed without reinsertion. The first and third balls drawn are placed in A, while the second and fourth in B.
Calculate the probability that urn A contains both balls marked with even numbers.

Place:

$$E_k = \{\text{la k-esima pallina estratta è pari}\}, \text{ con } k = 1, \ldots . 20.$$

We have:

$$P(E_k) = \frac{10}{20} = \frac{1}{2}.$$

Defined:

$$F = \{\text{l'urna A contiene tutte palline pari}\}$$

We find that its probability is equal to:

$$P(E_1 E_3) = P(E_3|E_1)P(E_1) = P(E_2')P(E_1) = \frac{9}{19} \cdot \frac{1}{2} = \frac{9}{38}$$

Exercise 30

An urn contains 10 dice, only 1 is loaded and is 1 with probability ½ and the other numbers with probability 1/10. A die is drawn from the urn and then rolled 3 times.

Let X be the random number that counts how many of the three rolls result in 1. Calculate the mean and variance of X.

Place:

$$E_k = \{\text{la k-esimo numero uscito è 1}\}, \text{ con } k = 1, 2, 3.$$

$$F = \{\text{Il dado estratto è truccato}\},$$

We have:

$$\mathbf{P}(F) = \tfrac{1}{10},$$

$$\mathbf{P}(E_k) = \mathbf{P}(E_k|F)\mathbf{P}(F) + \mathbf{P}(E_k|\tilde{F})\mathbf{P}(\tilde{F}) = \frac{1}{5}.$$

$$X = E_1 + E_2 + E_3,$$

The mean of X is:

$$\mathbf{P}(X) = \mathbf{P}(E_1) + P(E_2) + \mathbf{P}(E_3) = \frac{3}{5}.$$

Since the events are not independent, we have:

$$\mathbf{P}(E_j E_k) = \mathbf{P}(E_j E_k|F)\mathbf{P}(F) + \mathbf{P}(E_j E_k|\tilde{F})\mathbf{P}(\tilde{F}) = \left(\frac{1}{2}\right)^2 \frac{1}{10} + \left(\frac{1}{6}\right)^2 \frac{9}{10} = \frac{1}{20}$$

$$\mathbf{cov}(E_j, E_k) = \mathbf{P}(E_j E_k) - \mathbf{P}(E_j)\mathbf{P}(E_k) = \tfrac{1}{100}$$

Having calculated the covariance we have:

$$\sigma^2(X) = \sum_{k=1}^{3} \sigma^2(E_k) + 2\mathbf{cov}(E_1, E_2) + 2\mathbf{cov}(E_2, E_3) + 2\mathbf{cov}(E_1, E_3).$$

But:

$$\sigma^2(E_k) = \mathbf{P}(E_k)\mathbf{P}(\tilde{E}_k) = \tfrac{4}{25}$$

Substituting the known values, we get the variance of X:

$$\sigma^2(X) = \tfrac{27}{50}.$$

Exercise 31

A convoy consists of 5 non-communicating carriages.
Suppose they want to pick up 150 people randomly.
Determine the minimum number of seats per carriage so that the probability of passengers remaining standing is less than 0.01.

Given E the event that the i-th passenger gets on carriage A, the number of passengers getting on A is given by:

$$S_{150} = E_1 + E_2 + \cdots + E_{150}$$

The request is therefore:

$$P(S_{150} > x) < 0.01$$

Which is equivalent to:

$$P(S_{150} \leq x) \geq 0.99$$

The single variables E are distributed as Bernoulli with mean and variance given by:

$$E(E_i) = \tfrac{1}{5}$$
$$Var(E_i) = \tfrac{4}{5}.$$

Applying the central limit theorem, we have:

$$P(S_{150} < x) = P(\frac{S_{150} - 150\frac{1}{5}}{\sqrt{150\frac{1}{5}\frac{4}{5}}}) < \frac{x - 150\frac{1}{5}}{\sqrt{150\frac{1}{5}\frac{4}{5}}})$$

And then:

$$P(S_{150} \le x) = P(Z < \frac{x - 150\frac{1}{5}}{\sqrt{150\frac{1}{5}\frac{4}{5}}})$$

Where Z is given by a standard normal distribution.
From the tables of this distribution we have that the value left on the right is 0.01 and 2.34 therefore:

$$\frac{x - 150\frac{1}{5}}{\sqrt{150\frac{1}{5}\frac{4}{5}}} = 2.34$$

Or:

$$x \ge 41.47.$$

At least 42 seats must be available in each carriage.

Exercise 32

Airlines estimate that 5% of those who have booked flights do not show up for boarding and for this reason they overbook.
If a company has sold 240 tickets for a plane that seats only 233, what is the probability that all passengers who show up have a seat on the plane?

Said X the event to appear on the fly once the reservation has been made, X has Bernoulli distributions with parameter 0.95.
The sum of the 240 independent Bernoulli variables is given by:

$$Y = \sum_{i=1}^{240} X_i,$$

Applying the central limit theorem we obtain that Y has a normal distribution of parameters:

$$Y \sim N(240 \times 0.95, 240 \times 0.95 \times (1 - 0.95)).$$

The required probability is therefore:

$$P(Y \leq 233) = P(\frac{Y - 228}{3.3764} \leq \frac{233 - 228}{3.3764}) = P(Z \leq 1.48) = 0.9306$$

Exercise 33

A telephone exchange receives daily traffic which can be represented by a normal distribution with mean 25 and variance 4.
A sample of telephone data is extracted with reinsertion every 10 days.
What is the probability that the sample mean is greater than 27?
What about the probability that the sample variance is greater than 6.5?

The sample mean has the normal distribution, so the probability is:

$$Pr(\bar{X} > 27) = Pr(\frac{(\bar{X} - 25)}{2/\sqrt{10}}) > \frac{(27 - 25)}{2/\sqrt{10}}) = Pr(Z > 3.17) = 0.0008$$

The sample variance has a chi-squared distribution:

$$\frac{S^2}{\sigma^2}(n - 1) \sim \chi^2_{n-1},$$

And then:

$$Pr(S^2 > 6.5) \; = \; Pr\left(\chi^2_{n-1} > \frac{(n-1) \times 6.5}{4}\right)$$
$$= \; Pr(\chi^2_9 > 14.625) = 0.1$$

Exercise 34

100 real numbers are added, each of which is rounded to the nearest integer.
The rounding error is a random variable given by a uniform distribution in the interval [-0.5,0.5].
Determine a number such that, with probability greater than 0.99, the error on the sum lies in the interval between the negative and positive signs of the number.

Place:

X_k l'errore di arrotondamento sul $k-mo$ numero ($k = 1, ..., 100$).

We have that the distribution is uniform with mean and variance:

$$E(X_k) = 0$$
$$Var(X_k) = \frac{1}{12}.$$

Applying the central limit theorem to the error made on the sum of 100 numbers, we have:

$$P(-\epsilon \leq S_{100} \leq \epsilon) = P(-\frac{\sqrt{12}}{\sqrt{100}} \cdot \epsilon \leq \frac{\sqrt{12}}{\sqrt{100}} \cdot S_{100} \leq \frac{\sqrt{12}}{\sqrt{100}} \cdot \epsilon) = 2 \cdot F(\frac{\sqrt{12}}{\sqrt{100}} \cdot \epsilon) - 1$$

Where F is distributed as a standard normal.
As it requires:

$$P(-\epsilon \leq S_{100} \leq \epsilon) = 2 \cdot F(\frac{\sqrt{12}}{\sqrt{100}} \cdot \epsilon) - 1 \geq 0.99$$

From the tables of the normal it can be seen that the value that leaves 0.005 on the right is 2.58, i.e.:

$$\left(\frac{\sqrt{12}}{\sqrt{100}} \cdot \epsilon\right) \geq 2.58$$

So it will be:

$$\epsilon \geq 7.46.$$

Exercise 35

Let X be a random variable having a normal distribution with mean 4.35 and standard deviation of 0.59, find:

$$P(4 \leq X \leq 5)$$

We change variable:

$$Z = \frac{X - \mu}{\sigma}$$

Z has a standard normal distribution.

$$X = 4 \implies Z = \frac{4 - 4.35}{0.59} = -0.5932$$

$$X = 5 \implies Z = \frac{5 - 4.35}{0.59} = 1.1017$$

Then, using the standard normal tables:

$$P(4 \leq X \leq 5) = P(-0.59 \leq Z \leq 1.10) = F(1.10) - F(-0.59) =$$
$$= 0.8643 - 1 + F(0.59) = 0.5867$$

Exercise 36

The variable X has a normal distribution with a mean date and variance. Knowing that:

$$P(X > 9) = 0.9192 \qquad P(X < 11) = 0.7580$$

Calculate:

$$P(X > 10) .$$

We have:

$$P(X > 9) = 1 - P(X < 9) = 0.9192$$
$$P(X < 9) = 1 - 0.9192 = 0.0808$$

Standardizing the variable, we get:

$$P\left(Z < \frac{9-\mu}{\sigma} \right) = 0.0808 < 0.5 \quad \Rightarrow \quad \frac{9-\mu}{\sigma} < 0$$

$$P\left(Z < \frac{9-\mu}{\sigma} \right) = P\left(Z > -\frac{9-\mu}{\sigma} \right) = 1 - P\left(Z < -\frac{9-\mu}{\sigma} \right) = 0.0808$$

$$P\left(Z < -\frac{9-\mu}{\sigma} \right) = 1 - 0.0808 = 0.9192$$

$$P(X < 11) = P\left(Z < \frac{11-\mu}{\sigma} \right) = 0.7580$$

Using the table of the standard normal we therefore have:

$$\begin{cases} -\dfrac{9-\mu}{\sigma} = 1.4 \\[2mm] \dfrac{11-\mu}{\sigma} = 0.7 \end{cases}$$

Or:

$$\mu = \frac{31}{3} \qquad \sigma = \frac{20}{21} .$$

Now it is easy to calculate the required probability:

$$P(X > 10) = P\left(Z > \frac{10 - \frac{31}{3}}{\frac{20}{21}}\right) = P\left(Z > -\frac{7}{20}\right) = P(Z < 0.35) = 0.6368$$

46

STATISTICAL INFERENCE

Introduction

Statistical inference falls into two broad areas of interest: estimation theory and hypothesis testing.

At the basis of both areas is sampling understood as the choice of the sample of the statistical population: it can be random, probabilistic, reasoned or convenient.

The sampling methods depend on the probability distribution and on the random variables just described.

Estimation theory

The estimation theory allows to estimate parameters starting from measured data through a deterministic function called estimator.

There are various properties that characterize the quality of an estimator including correctness, consistency, efficiency, sufficiency, and completeness.

A correct estimator is a function that has an expected value equal to the quantity to be estimated, vice versa it is called biased.

The difference between the expected value of the estimator and that of the sample is called bias, if this difference is zero as the sample tends to infinity then the estimator is said to be asymptotically correct.

Given a random variable X of unknown parameter Y, an estimator T(X) is sufficient for Y if the conditional probability distribution of X given by T(X) does not depend on Y.

An estimator for the parameter Y is said to be weakly consistent if, as the sample size approaches infinity, it converges in probability to the value of Y.

If, on the other hand, it almost certainly converges, then it is said to be consistent in the strong sense.

A sufficient condition for weak consistency is that the estimator is asymptotically correct and that we have at the same time:

$$\lim_{n \to \infty} \text{var}(T_n(x)) = 0$$

We define Fisher information as the variance of the logarithmic derivative associated with a given likelihood function (we will define the concept of likelihood shortly).

$$I(\vartheta) = E\left[\left(\frac{\partial}{\partial \vartheta} \ln f(X; \vartheta)\right)^2\right]$$

This quantity is additive for independent random variables.
The Fisher information of a sufficient statistic is the same as that contained in the whole sample.
In the case of multivariate distributions we have:

$$I(\vartheta)_{m,\, n} = E\left[\frac{\partial}{\partial \vartheta_m} \ln f(X; \vartheta) \frac{\partial}{\partial \vartheta_n} \ln f(X; \vartheta)\right]$$

The Cramer-Rao inequality states that the variance of an unbiased estimator is thus related to the Fisher information:

$$\text{var}\left(\hat{\vartheta}\right) \geq \frac{1}{I(\vartheta)} = \frac{1}{E\left[\left(\frac{\partial}{\partial \vartheta} \ln f(X; \vartheta)\right)^2\right]}$$

In the multivariate case it becomes:

$$\text{cov}_{\vartheta}(T(x)) \geq I(\vartheta)^{-1}$$

The efficiency of an unbiased estimator is defined as follows:

$$e(T) = \frac{1}{I(\vartheta)\,\text{var}(T)}$$

It follows from the Cramer-Rao inequality that the efficiency for an unbiased estimator is less than or equal to 1.

An estimator is said to be efficient if its variance reaches the lower limit of the Cramer-Rao inequality and it is said to be asymptotically efficient if this value is reached as a limit.

The relative efficiency between two estimators is given by:

$$e(T_1, T_2, \vartheta) = \frac{E\left[(T_1 - \vartheta)^2\right]}{E\left[(T_2 - \vartheta)^2\right]}$$

The probability associated with the sample is given by the following probability distribution:

$$P\left(\{x_i\}_{i=1}^n \mid \vartheta\right) = L_D\left(\vartheta \mid \{x_i\}_{i=1}^n\right)$$

To estimate the parameter, the available data x that make up the sample can be used.

The maximum likelihood method searches for the most likely value of this parameter, i.e. that maximizes the probability of having obtained the sample.

In this case the function appearing on the second side of the previous relation is called the likelihood function and the estimator is called maximum likelihood:

$$\hat{\vartheta} = \arg\max_{\vartheta \in \Theta} L_D(\vartheta \mid x_1, \ldots, x_n)$$

One can choose such estimators to be correct or asymptotically correct.

Furthermore, the maximum likelihood estimator may not necessarily be unique for a given probability distribution.

Given a maximum likelihood estimator for one parameter, then the maximum likelihood estimator for another parameter that functionally depends on the first is given by applying the same function, provided it is bijective.

Maximum likelihood estimators do not reach the lower bound for the variance established by the Cramer-Rao inequality.

The likelihood function is a conditional probability function defined as follows:

$$L(b \mid A) = \alpha P(A \mid B = b)$$

Another method for finding estimators is the so-called method of moments.

Using this method, an estimator satisfies the conditions of one or more sample moments.
It must be said that the maximum likelihood estimators are more efficient than the moments method estimators.
A typical condition of the method of moments is the following:

$$E\big[f(x_i; \vartheta_0)\big] = 0$$

Another estimation method, fundamental for linear regression, is the least squares method which allows the identification of trend lines starting from experimental data so that the sum of the squares of the distances between these data and the estimated ones is minimal.
The estimators for the slope and intercept are given by:

$$\hat{\beta}_1 = \frac{s_{XY}}{s_X^2}$$

$$\hat{\beta}_0 = \overline{Y} - \hat{\beta}\overline{X}_1$$

Where we have, in the case of simple linear regression:

$$Y_i = \beta_0 + \beta_1 X_i + u_i$$

While for the multivariate case we have:

$$Y_i = \beta_0 + \beta_1 X_{1i} + \ldots + \beta_k X_{ki} + u_i$$

In both cases the statistical error, given by the last parameter u, has zero conditional mean.

The Rao-Blackwell estimator is defined as the conditional expected value of an estimator with respect to a sufficient statistic:

$$E\big[\delta(X) \mid T(X)\big]$$

The Rao-Blackwell theorem states the standard deviation of a Rao-Blackwell estimator is less than or equal to that of the original estimator:

$$E\big[(\delta_1(X) - \vartheta)^2\big] \le E\big[(\delta(X) - \vartheta)^2\big]$$

So the Rao-Blackwell estimator represents an improvement on the initial estimator.

An estimator is complete if for each measurable function:

$$E\big[g(s(X)\big] = 0 \Rightarrow \forall\, \vartheta,\, P_S(g(s(X)) = 0) = 1$$

The Lehmann-Scheffé theorem states that a correct, complete and sufficient estimator is a minimum variance correct estimator, i.e.:

$$\mathrm{var}(\delta(X_1,...,X_n)) \le \mathrm{var}(\tilde{\delta}(X_1,...,X_n))$$

The Gauss-Markov theorem states that, in a linear regression model having zero expected value error, the best corrected linear estimator is the least squares estimator.

A Bayes estimator is a function that minimizes the expected value of the posterior probability of a function, called loss.
Given a parameter with known prior probability distribution and called L a loss function, then the Bayes risk of the estimator is given by:

$$E_\pi\left\{L(\vartheta, \delta)\right\}$$

The Bayes estimator is the one that minimizes this value.
Under suitable conditions, for a large sample, the Bayes estimator is asymptotically unbiased and converges in distribution to the normal distribution with zero expected value and variance equal to the inverse of the Fisher information, therefore it is also asymptotically efficient.

Hypothesis testing

The second sector of statistical inference is the verification of hypotheses following a statistical test which can be parametric or non-parametric.
A test that can be applied in the presence of a given probability distribution of the data is called parametric, otherwise the test is called non-parametric.
A statistical test involves a statistical error that can be divided into two categories: the first type error is given by rejecting the hypothesis when it is true, the second type is given by accepting the hypothesis when it is false.

This hypothesis is called the null hypothesis or zero hypothesis.

The Neyman-Pearson fundamental lemma states that, given two simple hypotheses, the ratio of likelihood functions that reject the first hypothesis for the second hypothesis is given by:

$$P(\Lambda(X) \leq k \mid H_0) = \alpha \Rightarrow \Lambda(x) := \frac{L(\vartheta_0 \mid x)}{L(\vartheta_1 \mid x)} \leq k$$

And it represents the most powerful hypothesis test.
If this holds for any value of the parameter, then the test is said to be uniformly more powerful.
If we assume the null hypothesis to be true, then the p-value indicates the probability of getting a result equal to the one observed.
It indicates the minimum level of significance for which the null hypothesis is rejected.

The most common parametric tests are given by the Student test where the data distribution is the Student's t or the Fisher test where the data distribution is the Fisher-Snedecor one or the zeta test where the data distribution is a standard normal $N(0,1)$.
In a parametric test it is of fundamental importance to define the confidence interval, ie the range of plausible values for the parameter to be estimated or tested.
The Neyman setting for the confidence interval asserts that it is a set of parameters for which the null hypothesis is accepted.
The confidence level of the interval is given by 1 minus the significance level of the test.

There are many nonparametric tests, let's list some of particular importance.
The binomial test is applied to Bernoulli statistical samples and the probabilities are calculated when the null hypothesis is true.
A test for two dependent samples and to understand the evolution of the situation is the sign test which takes into consideration the difference (positive or negative) of the two samples based on the individual parameters.
Given a binary sequence, the sequence test is performed to verify the independence of the data.
The number of repeated sequences in a sequence of length N is a normal random variable of expected value and variance given by:

$$\mu = 1 + 2\frac{N^+ N^-}{N}$$

$$\sigma^2 = \frac{(\mu - 1)(\mu - 2)}{N - 1}$$

Where the quotes + and – indicate the positive or negative symbols of the sequence.

Budne's test tests the null hypothesis that two data sets come from two random variables having the same distribution.

The Kolmogorov-Smirnov test tests the shape of sampling distributions and is a nonparametric alternative to the Student test.

The Kruskal-Wallis test tests the medians of different samples for equality.

Pearson's chi-squared test is applied to verifying whether a sample was drawn from a population having a given probability distribution.

If the distribution is binomial then the binomial test can be applied; moreover, if there are at most two samples, the Kolmogorov-Smirnov test can also be applied.

A special case of Pearson's chi-squared test is the median test, which tests the null hypothesis that the medians of two samples are equal.

Fisher's exact test is used if the variables are Bernoulli and the samples are small.

The Q test is used to discard or reject statistical data that are not in line with the sample parameters and, therefore, are possible errors.

The Shapiro-Wilk test is used to test the normality of small samples by comparing two estimators for the sample variance.

Regression

A fundamental problem in statistics is regression, i.e. the functional relationship between the measured variables extracted from a potentially infinite sample.

In particular, linear regression is a method of estimating the conditional expected value of a dependent variable Y, once the values of other independent variables X (also called regressors) are known.

The case of simple linear regression is formulated as follows:

$$Y_i = \beta_0 + \beta_1 X_i + u_i$$

The beta values have already been presented as intercept and slope, plus u is the statistical error.
As we have seen, it is possible to estimate these values using the least squares method.
In the case of multiple linear regression, the relationship is as follows:

$$Y_i = \beta_0 + \beta_1 X_{1i} + \ldots + \beta_k X_{ki} + u_i$$

The method of least squares allows to find an estimate of the dependent variable which is an orthogonal projection of the vector of observations y on the space generated by the columns of the matrix describing the X independent variables.
The coefficient of determination measures the goodness of fit of the linear regression and is:

$$R^2 = \frac{\sum_i (\hat{y}_i - \bar{y})^2}{\sum_i (y_i - \bar{y})^2}$$

There is also a nonlinear regression that applies to a model of the general form:

$$Y = f(X; \vartheta) + \varepsilon$$

In this case the estimation methods resort to numerical optimization algorithms or linearization processes, introducing an additional error with respect to the statistical error.

Bayesian inference

From Bayes' theorem derives the Bayesian inference approach in which the probabilities are interpreted as levels of confidence for the occurrence of a given event.
In Bayesian statistics, Bayes' theorem takes this form:

$$P(H_0 \mid E) = \frac{P(E \mid H_0) P(H_0)}{P(E)}$$

Where E denotes the observed empirical data, while H_0 it is the null hypothesis, $P(H_0)$ it is called the prior probability, $P(E)$ it is the marginal probability, $P(H_0|E)$ it is the posterior probability, $P(E|H_0)$ it is the likelihood function.
The likelihood ratio is called:

$$\Lambda = \frac{L(H_0 \mid E)}{L(notH_0 \mid E)} = \frac{P(E \mid H_0)}{P(E \mid notH_0)}$$

If X is distributed as a binomial random variable having a parameter distributed a priori as a beta then the same parameter distributed a posteriori also follows a beta distribution (obviously with different characteristic parameters).
The same is true if X is distributed as a negative binomial random variable.
If X is distributed as a gamma variable having the second parameter distributed a priori as a gamma then the same parameter distributed posteriorly also follows a gamma.
The same is true if X is distributed as a Poissonian or as a normal one.

Exercises

Exercise 1

Given a sample set made up of 100 samples, one is chosen at random and the value of 12 is found.
Assume that these values are distributed according to a normal of unknown mean and variance equal to 4.
Propose an unbiased estimator for the mean and find out what its variance is.
Determine the confidence interval for the mean at the 0.95 level.
Determine the same interval without however assuming a normal distribution.

An unbiased estimator is given by the sample mean.
The variance of this estimator tends to zero as the number of samples tends to infinity. We have:

$$Var(\bar{X}) = Var\left(\frac{\sum_{i=1}^{n} X_i}{n}\right)$$

$$= \frac{1}{n^2} \sum_{i=1}^{100} Var(X_i)$$

$$= \frac{n}{n^2} Var(X_i) = \frac{1}{n}\sigma^2$$

And then:

$$Var(\bar{X}) = \frac{1}{100}\sigma^2 = \frac{1}{100} \times 4 = \frac{1}{25}$$

Given the confidence interval, we have:

$$1-\alpha = 0.95 \rightarrow \alpha = 0.05 \rightarrow \alpha/2 = 0.025 \rightarrow$$

$$\Phi(z_{\alpha/2}) = 1-\alpha/2 = 0.975 \rightarrow z_{\alpha/2} = 1.96$$

Since:

$$\bar{X} \sim N(\mu, \sigma^2/n)$$

$$\frac{\bar{X}-\mu}{\sigma/\sqrt{n}} \sim N(0,1)$$

The range is:

$$95\% IC = [l_1, l_2] = \left[\bar{x} - z_{\alpha/2}\frac{\sigma}{\sqrt{n}}; \bar{x} + z_{\alpha/2}\frac{\sigma}{\sqrt{n}}\right]$$

$$= \left[12 - 1.96\frac{2}{10}; 12 + 1.96\frac{2}{10}\right] = [11.608; 12.392].$$

According to the central limit theorem, this interval remains valid even in the absence of a normal distribution.

Exercise 2

Taking a sample of 25 elements we have:

$$\sum_{i=1}^{25} x_i = 2450.$$

Where each x has a normal distribution with unknown mean and variance equal to 64.
Determine the confidence interval for the mean at the 0.9 level.
Determine the minimum sample size that ensures that the confidence level 0.9 has a length of less than 10.

The estimate of the sample mean is:

$$\bar{x} = \frac{1}{25} \sum_{i=1}^{25} x_i = 2450/25 = 98.$$

$$\mathbb{E}(\bar{X}) = \mu; \quad Var(\bar{X}) = \sigma^2/n,$$

$$\bar{X} \sim N(\mu, 64/25)$$

Given that:

$$1-\alpha = 0.90 \rightarrow \alpha = 0.10 \rightarrow \alpha/2 = 0.05 \rightarrow$$

$$\Phi(z_{\alpha/2}) = 1-\alpha/2 = 0.95 \rightarrow z_{\alpha/2} = 1.645.$$

The confidence interval is:

$$90\% IC = [l_1, l_2] = \left[\bar{x} - z_{\alpha/2} \frac{\sigma}{\sqrt{n}}; \bar{x} + z_{\alpha/2} \frac{\sigma}{\sqrt{n}} \right]$$

$$= \left[98 - 1.645\frac{8}{5}; 98 + 1.645\frac{8}{5} \right] = [95.368; 100.632].$$

To enforce that the length of this interval is less than 10, proceed as follows:

$$2 \cdot z_{\alpha/2} \frac{\sigma}{\sqrt{n}} < 10 \Leftrightarrow 2 \cdot z_{0.05} \frac{8}{\sqrt{n}} < 10 \Leftrightarrow$$

$$\Leftrightarrow 2 \cdot 1.645 \frac{8}{\sqrt{n}} < 10 \Leftrightarrow 2 \cdot 1.645 \frac{8}{10} < \sqrt{n} \Leftrightarrow$$

$$\Leftrightarrow \left(2 \cdot 1.645 \frac{8}{10}\right)^2 < n \Rightarrow n > 6.93.$$

And therefore you must have a minimum of 7 samples.

Exercise 3

Given a sample of 60 pieces, defects and weight were found for each of them.
25 pieces are defective and the weights have the following properties:

$$\sum_{i=1}^{60} x_i = 840.$$

$$\sum_{i=1}^{60} x_i^2 = 12300.$$

Propose an unbiased estimator for the mean.
Propose an unbiased estimator for the variance.
Propose a 99% confidence interval in case X is distributed as a normal.
Propose a 99% confidence interval in case X is not distributed as a normal.
Propose a 95% confidence interval for the mean value of Bernoulli's random variable Y which assumes value 1 if the piece is defective and 0 otherwise.

An unbiased estimator for the mean is the sample mean:

$$\bar{x} = \frac{1}{60} \sum_{i=1}^{60} x_i = 840/60 = 14.$$

$$Var[\bar{X}] = \frac{1}{n}\sigma^2.$$

This estimator converges in probability.
An unbiased estimator for the variance is the sample variance.

$$S^2 = \frac{1}{n-1}\sum_{i=1}^{n}(X_i - \bar{X})^2.$$

$$S^2 = \frac{1}{n-1}\sum_{i=1}^{n}(x_i - \bar{x})^2 = \frac{1}{n-1}\left[\sum_{i=1}^{n}x_i^2 - n\bar{x}^2\right]$$

$$= \frac{1}{59}\left(\sum_{i=1}^{60}x_i^2 - n\bar{x}^2\right) = \frac{1}{59}\left(12300 - 60\cdot 14^2\right) = 540/59 = 9.15.$$

We have:

$$\frac{\bar{X} - \mu}{S\sqrt{n}} \sim t_{n-1}$$

Given that:

$$1 - \alpha = 0.99 \to \alpha = 0.01 \to \alpha/2 = 0.005 \to$$
$$P(t_{59} \le t_{59,\alpha/2}) = 1 - \alpha/2 = 0.995$$
$$\to P(t_{59} \ge t_{59,\alpha/2}) = \alpha/2 = 0.005 \to t_{59,\alpha/2} = 2.66,$$

The confidence interval is:

$$99\% IC = [l_1, l_2] = \left[\bar{x} - t_{59,\alpha/2}\frac{S}{\sqrt{n}}; \bar{x} + t_{59,\alpha/2}\frac{S}{\sqrt{n}}\right]$$

$$= \left[14 - 2.66\frac{3.02}{7.75}; 14 + 2.66\frac{3.02}{7.75}\right] = [12.96; 15.04].$$

By the central limit theorem, this interval exists even in the case of non-normal distribution.
Finally, for Bernoulli's variable Y we can reason in this way.
The proportion of defective parts is:

$$\hat{p} = 25/60 = 0.417.$$

By the central limit theorem, we can say that:

$$(\hat{p} \sim N(\pi; \pi(1-\pi)/n)).$$

An estimate of its variance is given by:

$$\hat{\sigma}^2 = \hat{p}(1-\hat{p})/n.$$

The required confidence interval is:

$$95\% IC \simeq [l_1, l_2] = \left[p - z_{\alpha/2}\sqrt{\frac{p(1-p)}{n}}; p + z_{\alpha/2}\sqrt{\frac{p(1-p)}{n}} \right]$$
$$= [0.417 - 1.96 \cdot 0.063; 0.417 + 1.96 \cdot 0.063] = [0.29; 0.54].$$

Exercise 4

Given a set of samples we have:

$$\sum_{i=1}^{9} x_i = 175.5.$$

$$\sum_{i=1}^{9} x_i^2 = 4222.25.$$

Where the single x's are distributed with a normal of unknown mean and variance.
Propose an unbiased estimator for the mean.
Propose an unbiased estimator for the variance.
Determine the 99% confidence interval for the mean.

An unbiased estimator for the mean is the sample mean:

$$\bar{X} = \frac{\sum_{i=1}^{n} X_i}{n}.$$

In the specific case

$$\bar{x} = \frac{\sum_{i=1}^{n} x_i}{n} = 175.5/9 = 19.5$$

And its variance tends to zero as n increases, in fact:

$$\mathbb{V}ar(\bar{X}) = \sigma^2/n$$

An unbiased estimator for the variance is the sample variance.

$$
\begin{aligned}
S^2 &= \frac{\sum_{i=1}^{n}(x_i - \bar{x})^2}{n-1} = \\
&= \frac{\sum_{i=1}^{n}(x_i)^2 - n(\bar{x})^2}{n-1} = \\
&= \frac{4222.25 - 9(19.5)^2}{8} = \\
&= 800/8 = 100
\end{aligned}
$$

Since:

$$\frac{\bar{X} - \mu}{S/\sqrt{n}} \sim t_{n-1}$$

$$1 - \alpha = 0.99 \rightarrow \alpha = 0.01 \rightarrow \alpha/2 = 0.005 \rightarrow$$
$$P(t_8 \le t_{8,\alpha/2}) = 1 - \alpha/2 = 0.995$$
$$\rightarrow P(t_8 \ge t_{8,\alpha/2}) = \alpha/2 = 0.005 \rightarrow t_{8,\alpha/2} = 3.355,$$

The 99% confidence interval is:

$$99\% IC = \left[\bar{x} - t_{n-1;\alpha/2} \frac{S}{\sqrt{n}} ; \bar{x} + t_{n-1;\alpha/2} \frac{S}{\sqrt{n}} \right] =$$

$$= \left[\bar{x} - t_{8;0.005} \frac{S}{\sqrt{n}} ; \bar{x} + t_{8;0.005} \frac{S}{\sqrt{n}} \right] =$$

$$= \left[19.5 - 3.355 \frac{10}{\sqrt{9}} ; 19.5 + 3.355 \frac{10}{\sqrt{9}} \right] = [8.317; 30.683].$$

Exercise 5

How does the width of the confidence interval change as the confidence level decreases?

The amplitude decreases, in fact if for example we consider a confidence interval for the mean with known variance:

$$IC = \left\{ \bar{x} - z_{1-\alpha/2} \sqrt{\frac{\sigma^2}{n}} ; \bar{x} + z_{1-\alpha/2} \sqrt{\frac{\sigma^2}{n}} \right\}$$

Exercise 6

Given a set of 30 samples with variance given by:

$$\sum_{i=1}^{30} (x_i - \bar{x})^2 = 25,$$

Assume that they have the normal distribution.
Determine a 90% confidence interval for the variance.

We simply have:

$$90\%IC \;=\; \left[\frac{(n-1)S^2}{\chi^2_{0.05;29}};\;\frac{(n-1)S^2}{\chi^2_{0.95;29}}\right] =$$

$$=\; \left[\frac{29\cdot 25}{42.557};\;\frac{29\cdot 25}{17.708}\right] = (17.036;\,40.94)$$

Exercise 7

Determine which of the two estimators S and T is biased and which is the more efficient in the following cases:

1. $\mathbb{E}(S) = \theta + 2,\; Var(S) = 3,\; \mathbb{E}(T) = \theta,\; Var(T) = 8;$

2. $\mathbb{E}(S) = \theta + 2,\; Var(S) = 5,\; \mathbb{E}(T) = \theta - 1,\; Var(T) = 6;$

3. $\mathbb{E}(S) = \theta,\; Var(S) = 6,\; \mathbb{E}(T) = \theta - 1,\; Var(T) = 4.$

Typically, the mean squared error of an estimator is:

$$EQM[T(X)] = Var(T(X)) + [\mathbb{E}(T(X)) - \theta]^2,$$

In the first case we have:

$$EQM(S) = (\theta + 2 - \theta)^2 + Var(S) = 3 + 2^2 = 7,$$
$$EQM(T) = Var(T) = 8.$$

The estimator S is the most efficient. T is not biased, S is.
In the second case we have:

$$EQM(S) = (\theta + 2 - \theta)^2 + Var(S) = 5 + 2^2 = 9,$$
$$EQM(T) = (\theta - 1 - \theta)^2 +$$
$$Var(T) = 6 + 1^2 = 7.$$

Both estimators are biased, T being the more efficient.
In the third case:

$$EQM(S) = Var(S) = 6,$$
$$EQM(T) = (\theta - 1 - \theta)^2 + Var(T) = 1^2 + 4 = 5.$$

S is not biased, T is. T is the most efficient.

Exercise 8

Given a population distributed according to a Bernoullian of given parameter, we have an estimator:

$$T(X) = \frac{X_1 + 2X_2 + X_3}{5},$$

Determine if the estimator is correct. If not, calculate the distortion. Calculate the mean squared error of T.

Since:

$$X \sim Ber(\pi),$$

So:

$$X_1, X_2, X_3 \sim Ber(\pi)$$
$$\mathbb{E}(X_i) = \pi$$
$$Var(X_i) = \pi(1 - \pi).$$
$$\mathbb{E}(T(X)) = \mathbb{E}\left(\frac{X_1 + 2X_2 + X_3}{5}\right) =$$
$$= \frac{\mathbb{E}(X_1) + 2\mathbb{E}(X_2) + \mathbb{E}(X_3)}{5} = \frac{\pi + 2\pi + \pi}{5} = \frac{4\pi}{5}.$$

The estimator is incorrect. Its distortion is:

$$d(T(X)) = 4/5\pi - \pi = -1/5\pi.$$

The variance of the estimator is:

$$Var(T(X)) = Var\left(\frac{X_1 + 2X_2 + X_3}{5}\right) = \frac{Var(X_1) + 4Var(X_2) + Var(X_3)}{25} =$$

$$= \frac{\pi(1-\pi) + 4\pi(1-\pi) + \pi(1-\pi)}{25} = \frac{6\pi(1-\pi)}{25}.$$

And then the mean squared error is given by:

$$EQM(T(X)) = d(T(X))^2 + Var(T(X)) = \frac{1}{25}\pi^2 + \frac{6\pi(1-\pi)}{25}$$

Exercise 9

Given two independent random variables extracted from a normal population of given mean and variance, consider as an estimator of the variance:

$$T_2 = X_1^2 - X_1 X_2$$

Determine if it is correct. If not, calculate the distortion.

$$\mathbb{E}(X^2) = Var(X) + [\mathbb{E}(X)]^2 = \sigma^2 + \mu^2.$$

$$\mathbb{E}(X_1 X_2) = \mathbb{E}(X_1)\mathbb{E}(X_2) = \mu \cdot \mu = \mu^2$$

$$\mathbb{E}[T_2(X)] = \mathbb{E}(X_1^2 - X_1 X_2) = \mathbb{E}(X_1^2) - \mathbb{E}(X_1 X_2)$$
$$= \sigma^2 + \mu^2 - \mu^2 = \sigma^2.$$

Therefore, the estimator is correct.

Exercise 10

Given a population with unknown mean and variance, consider as an estimator of the mean:

$$T_n = 1/3X_1 + 1/3X_2 + \ldots + 1/3X_n.$$

Find for which values of n the estimator is correct.
How does the variance behave as n increases?

The estimator is correct for n=3.

$$\mathbb{E}(T_n) = \mathbb{E}(1/3X_1 + 1/3X_2 + \ldots + 1/3X_n) = 1/3n\,\mathbb{E}(X) = 1/3n\mu$$

$$1/3n\mu = \mu \rightarrow 1/3n = 1$$

$$\mathrm{Var}(T_n) = \mathrm{Var}(1/3X_1 + 1/3X_2 + \ldots + 1/3X_n) = 1/9n\sigma^2$$

So the variance grows with n.

Exercise 11

Given a population with unknown mean and variance, calculate the mean squared error of the following estimator of the mean:

$$T_n = \frac{1}{4}X_1 + \frac{3}{4}\left(\frac{X_2 + \ldots + X_n}{n-1}\right).$$

Given that:

$$\mathbb{E}(T_n) = \mathbb{E}\left[\frac{1}{4}X_1 + \frac{3}{4}\left(\frac{X_2 + \ldots + X_n}{n-1}\right)\right] =$$

$$= \frac{1}{4}\mathbb{E}(X_1) + \frac{3}{4}\mathbb{E}\left(\frac{X_2 + \ldots + X_n}{n-1}\right) =$$

$$= \frac{1}{4}\mu + \frac{3}{4}\mu = \mu,$$

You will have:

$$EQM(T) = Var(T) = \frac{1}{16}Var(X_1) + \frac{9}{16}Var\left(\frac{X_2 + \ldots + X_n}{n-1}\right) =$$

$$= \frac{1}{16}\sigma^2 + \frac{9}{16}\frac{(n-1)}{(n-1)^2}\sigma^2 = \frac{(n+8)}{16(n-1)}\sigma^2$$

Exercise 12

Check whether the following estimator of the mean value of a random variable X is consistent in probability:

$$0.8 \cdot X_1 + \frac{0.2}{n-1}\cdot X_2 + \frac{0.2}{n-1}\cdot X_3 + \cdots + \frac{0.2}{n-1}\cdot X_n$$

An estimator is consistent in probability if:

$$\lim_{n\to\infty} P(|T_n - \theta| < \epsilon) = 1.$$

By Chebyshev's inequality, an estimator is consistent in probability if it is asymptotically unbiased and if its variance tends to zero as n tends to infinity, i.e.:

$$\lim_{n\to\infty} E(T_n - \theta) = 0$$

$$\lim_{n\to\infty} E(T_n - \theta)^2 = \lim_{n\to\infty} Var(T_n) = 0.$$

Let's see if the estimator is unbiased:

$$E(T_n) = 0.8 \cdot E(X_1) + \frac{0.2}{n-1}\cdot E(X_2) + \frac{0.2}{n-1}\cdot X_3 + \cdots + \frac{0.2}{n-1}\cdot E(X_n)$$

$$= 0.8 \cdot \mu + 0.2 \cdot \frac{n-1}{n-1}\cdot \mu = \mu$$

It's actually not distorted. Moreover,

$$Var(T_n) = 0.8^2 \cdot Var(X_1) + \frac{0.2^2}{(n-1)^2}\cdot E(X_2) + \frac{0.2^2}{(n-1)^2}\cdot X_3 + \cdots + \frac{0.2^2}{(n-1)^2}\cdot E(X_n) =$$

$$= (0.64 + \frac{0.04}{(n-1)})\cdot\sigma^2$$

Since this variance does not tend to zero as n tends to infinity, it is not possible to apply what has been said above and therefore the given estimator is not consistent in probability.

Exercise 13

Given a normal population of unknown mean and unit variance, draw a sample of 2 units. Given the following estimators for the mean:

$$T_{1,2} = \tfrac{2}{3}X_1 + \tfrac{1}{3}X_2$$

$$T_{2,2} = \tfrac{1}{2}X_1 + \tfrac{1}{2}X_2$$

Check if they are correct, determine the most efficient and calculate the efficiency ratio.

We compute the expected values of the estimators:

$$
\begin{aligned}
\mathbb{E}(T_{1,2}) &= \mathbb{E}\left(\frac{2}{3}X_1 + \frac{1}{3}X_2\right) = \\
&= \frac{2}{3}\mathbb{E}(X_1) + \frac{1}{3}\mathbb{E}(X_2) \\
&= \frac{2}{3}\mu + \frac{1}{3}\mu = \mu
\end{aligned}
$$

$$
\begin{aligned}
\mathbb{E}(T_{2,2}) &= \mathbb{E}\left(\frac{1}{2}X_1 + \frac{1}{2}X_2\right) = \\
&= \frac{1}{2}\mathbb{E}(X_1) + \frac{1}{2}\mathbb{E}(X_2) \\
&= \frac{1}{2}\mu + \frac{1}{2}\mu = \mu
\end{aligned}
$$

Both are correct. The mean squared errors are:

$$EQM(T_{1,2}) = Var(T_{1,2}) = Var\left(\frac{2}{3}X_1 + \frac{1}{3}X_2\right) =$$

$$= \frac{4}{9}Var(X_1) + \frac{1}{9}Var(X_2)$$

$$= \frac{4}{9}\sigma^2 + \frac{1}{9}\sigma^2 = \frac{5}{9}\sigma^2,$$

$$EQM(T_{2,2}) = Var(T_{2,2}) = Var\left(\frac{1}{2}X_1 + \frac{1}{2}X_2\right) =$$

$$= \frac{1}{4}Var(X_1) + \frac{1}{4}Var(X_2)$$

$$= \frac{1}{4}\sigma^2 + \frac{1}{4}\sigma^2 = \frac{1}{2}\sigma^2,$$

So the more efficient is the second one.
The efficiency ratio is:

$$e = \frac{EQM(T_{1,n})}{EQM(T_{2,n})} = \frac{Var(T_{1,n})}{Var(T_{2,n})} = \frac{5/9\sigma^2}{1/2\sigma^2} = 10/9$$

Exercise 14

Given a population, is a part of it distinguishable with a given characteristic.
Given the estimator for this part of the population:

$$T = \frac{1}{4}X_1 + \frac{3}{4}X_2$$

Determine if it is correct.
Calculate its variance if the population share is 0.3.

The population is distributed according to a Bernoulli law:

$$(X \sim Ber(\pi),$$

Therefore:

$$E(T) = E(\frac{1}{4}X_1 + \frac{3}{4}X_2) = \frac{1}{4}E(X_1) + \frac{3}{4}E(X_2) = \frac{1}{4}\pi + \frac{3}{4}\pi = \pi$$

So the estimator is correct.
Also, its variance is:

$$Var(T) = \frac{1}{16}Var(X_1) + \frac{9}{16}Var(X_2) = \frac{1}{16}\pi(1-\pi) + \frac{9}{16}\pi(1-\pi) = \frac{10}{16}\pi(1-\pi)$$

Which for 0.3 holds:

$$Var(T) = 0.13.$$

Exercise 15

Given a population with normal distribution of unknown mean and variance 256, the mean value is assumed to be 100.
After 64 samples were extracted, an average value of 106 was found.
We want to test the null hypothesis:

$$H_0 : \mu = 100$$

Against the alternative:

$$H_1 : \mu > 100,$$

With a significance value of 0.05.
Determine the acceptance regions and critical region for this test.

The data of the problem are:

$$X \sim N(\mu, 256), \quad \bar{x} = 106, \quad n = 64,$$
$$\alpha = 0.05$$

And the hypothesis is:

$$\begin{cases} H_0 : \mu = 100 \\ H_1 : \mu > 100, \end{cases}$$

We note that:

$$T_n = \frac{\bar{X} - \mu_0}{\sigma/\sqrt{n}} \sim N(0, 1)$$

We reject the null hypothesis and verify the test.
Given that:

$$\alpha = 0.05 \rightarrow \Phi(z_{0.05}) = 1 - 0.05 = 0.95 \rightarrow z_\alpha = 1.645,$$

We have:

$$R.A. : \frac{\bar{x} - \mu_0}{\sigma/\sqrt{n}} \leq 1.645$$

$$R.C. : \frac{\bar{x} - \mu_0}{\sigma/\sqrt{n}} > 1.645.$$

And they are the acceptance and critical regions, respectively.
The observed value of the test statistic under the null hypothesis is:

$$t_n = \frac{\bar{x} - \mu_0}{\sigma/\sqrt{n}} = \frac{106 - 100}{\sqrt{256/64}} = \frac{6}{2} = 3$$

Belonging to the critical region, we reject the null hypothesis.

Exercise 16

Given a population distributed as a Gaussian random variable of unknown mean and variance 3, draw a random sample of 3 items to test the null hypothesis against the alternative:

$$\begin{cases} H_0 : \mu = 2 \\ H_1 : \mu = 1. \end{cases}$$

Given the following critical region:

$$R.C. : \{(x_1, x_2, x_3) : 2x_1 - 2x_2 + x_3 < 1.2\}.$$

Calculate the probability of the first and second type errors.

The test statistic is:

$$T(\mathbf{X}) = 2X_1 - 2X_2 + X_3 \sim N(\mu; 27).$$

Considering that:

$$\mathbb{E}(T(\mathbf{X})) = 2\mu - 2\mu + \mu = \mu.$$

$$\begin{aligned} Var(T(\mathbf{X})) &= Var(2X_1 - 2X_2 + X_3) \\ &= 4Var(X_1) + 4Var(X_2) + Var(X_3) \\ &= 9Var(X) = 27. \end{aligned}$$

The probability of an error of the first type is given by:

$$\begin{aligned} \alpha &= P(\text{errore di I tipo}) = P(\text{respingere } H_0 | H_0) = \\ & P(2X_1 - 2X_2 + X_3 < 1.2 | \mu = 2) \end{aligned}$$

$$= P\left(\frac{2X_1 - 2X_2 + X_3 - \mu}{\sqrt{27}} < \frac{1.2 - \mu}{\sqrt{27}}\Big|\mu = 2\right)$$

$$= P(Z < \frac{1.2 - 2}{5.2})$$

$$= P(Z < -0.15) = \Phi(-0.15) = 1 - \Phi(0.15) = 0.4404.$$

The acceptance region will be:

$$R.A. : \{(x_1, x_2, x_3) : 2x_1 - 2x_2 + x_3 \geq 1.2\}.$$

And so the probability for an error of the second kind is:

$$\beta = P(\text{errore di II tipo}) = P(\text{non respingere } H_0|H_1) =$$

$$P(2X_1 - 2X_2 + X_3 \geq 1.2|\mu = 1)$$

$$= Pr(\frac{2X_1 - 2X_2 + X_3 - \mu}{\sqrt{27}} \geq \frac{1.2 - \mu}{\sqrt{27}}\Big|\mu = 1)$$

$$= Pr(Z \geq \frac{1.2 - 1}{5.2})$$

$$= Pr(Z \geq 0.038) = 1 - \Phi(0.038) = 0.484.$$

Exercise 17

In a sample of 15 items, the mean value is 28.5 and the variance is 16. Assuming that the population is distributed according to a normal with mean 25 and unknown variance, verify:

$$Ipotesi \begin{cases} H_0 : \mu \leq 25 \\ H_1 : \mu > 25 \end{cases}$$

With a probability of error of the first type of 0.025.

We have:

$$\hat{\sigma} = S = 4, \qquad \bar{x} = 28.50, \qquad n = 15, \qquad \alpha = 0.025$$

We use the t-student as it uses an unbiased estimate of the variance:

$$T_n = \frac{\bar{X} - \mu_0}{S/\sqrt{n}} \sim t_{n-1}$$

We reject the null hypothesis.
Given that:

$$\alpha = 0.025 \rightarrow P(t_{14} \geq t_{14,\alpha}) = 0.025 \rightarrow t_{14,\alpha} = 2.145.$$

The regions of acceptance and criticism are:

$$R.A. : \frac{\bar{x} - \mu_0}{S/\sqrt{n}} \leq 2.145$$

$$R.C. : \frac{\bar{x} - \mu_0}{S/\sqrt{n}} > 2.145.$$

The observed value of the test statistic under the null hypothesis:

$$t_n = \frac{\bar{x} - \mu_0}{S/\sqrt{n}} = \frac{28.5 - 25}{4/\sqrt{15}} = 3.39$$

It falls into the critical region and therefore it is correct to reject the null hypothesis.

Exercise 18

Given a population distributed according to a normal distribution with unknown mean and variance, extract a sample of 10 items which have mean and variance equal to 12 and 16.
Find a confidence interval for the mean at the 0.95 level.

Test the hypothesis:

$$H_0 : \mu = 13$$

Against the alternative at the 0.05 level.
What if the level is 0.01?

The distribution for the estimator of the mean is one of t-students with n-1 degrees of freedom.
The central limit theorem cannot be applied as there are only 10 reference samples.
The confidence interval sought is:

$$
\begin{aligned}
95\%CI \; &= \; [l_1, l_2] = \left[\bar{x} - t_{n-1;\alpha/2} \frac{S}{\sqrt{n}} ; \bar{x} + t_{n-1;\alpha/2} \frac{S}{\sqrt{n}} \right] = \\
&= \left[\bar{x} - t_{9;0.025} \frac{S}{\sqrt{n}} ; \bar{x} + t_{9;0.025} \frac{S}{\sqrt{n}} \right] = \\
&= \left[12 - 2.262 \frac{4}{\sqrt{10}} ; 12 + 2.262 \frac{4}{\sqrt{10}} \right] = [9.14; 14.86].
\end{aligned}
$$

The test is as follows:

$$
\begin{cases}
H_0 : \mu = 13 \\
H_1 : \mu \neq 13.
\end{cases}
$$

The critical region is:

$$
R.C. : \; = \; \left| \frac{\bar{x} - \mu_0}{S/\sqrt{n}} \right| > t_{9,0.025} ,
$$

The critical value is:

$$
P(t_{n-1} < -t_{n-1,\alpha/2}) = P(t_{n-1} > t_{n-1,\alpha/2}) = \, \cdot
$$

$$
\alpha/2 = 0.025 \rightarrow t_{n-1,\alpha/2} = 2.262
$$

Then the rejection region is given by:

$$R.C. : \begin{cases} \frac{\bar{x} - \mu_0}{S/\sqrt{n}} > 2.262 \\ \frac{\bar{x} - \mu_0}{S/\sqrt{n}} < -2.262 \end{cases}$$

The value of the test statistic is:

$$t_n = \frac{\bar{x} - \mu_0}{S/\sqrt{n}} = \frac{12 - 13}{4/\sqrt{10}} = -0.79$$

Since we do not belong to the critical region, we cannot reject the null hypothesis.
Decreasing the error level to 0.01 does not change anything.

Exercise 19

Given a population with mean 37 and standard deviation 10, we extract 400 samples whose mean is 36. With a significance level of 1%, can we reject the hypothesis that the true mean is 37?

We have:

$$\sigma = 10, \qquad \bar{x} = 36, \qquad n = 400, \qquad \alpha = 0.01$$

$$\begin{cases} H_0 : \mu_0 = 37 \\ H_1 : \mu_0 \neq 37 \end{cases}$$

Given the large number of samples, the central limit theorem can be used.
Therefore:

$$T_n = \frac{\bar{X} - \mu_0}{\sigma/\sqrt{n}} \simeq N(0, 1)$$

The critical region is:

$$R.C.: \quad = \quad \left| \frac{\bar{x} - \mu_0}{\sigma/\sqrt{n}} \right| > z_{\alpha/2},$$

Given that:

$$\alpha = 0.01 \rightarrow \alpha/2 = 0.005 \rightarrow \Phi(z_{0.005}) = 1 - 0.005 = 0.995 \rightarrow z_{\alpha/2} = 2.575.$$

We have:

$$R.C.: \quad = \quad \left| \frac{\bar{x} - \mu_0}{\sigma/\sqrt{n}} \right| > 2.575.$$

The value of the test statistic under the null hypothesis is:

$$t_n = \frac{\bar{x} - \mu_0}{\sigma/\sqrt{n}} = \frac{36 - 37}{10/\sqrt{400}} = -2$$

Since we do not fall into the critical region, we cannot reject the null hypothesis.

Exercise 20

Given a population, take 400 samples of which 240 are defective.
Propose a critical region to test the following hypothesis at a significance level of 1%:

$$\begin{cases} H_0 : \pi = 0.5 \\ H_1 : \pi < 0.5. \end{cases}$$

We have:

$$X = \text{difettosità} \sim Ber(\pi); \quad \hat{p} = 240/400 = 0.6; \quad \alpha = 0.01; \quad n = 400.$$

Since the number of samples is large, the central limit theorem can be used.

The test statistic is:

$$T_n = \frac{\dot{p} - \pi_0}{\sqrt{\pi_0(1 - \pi_0)/n}} \simeq N(0, 1).$$

The critical region and the acceptance region are:

$$R.C. := \frac{\dot{p} - \pi_0}{\sqrt{\pi_0(1 - \pi_0)/n}} < -z_\alpha$$

$$R.A. := \frac{\dot{p} - \pi_0}{\sqrt{\pi_0(1 - \pi_0)/n}} \geq -z_\alpha$$

Since:

$$\alpha = 0.01 \rightarrow \Phi(z_{0.01}) = 1 - 0.01 = 0.99 \rightarrow z_\alpha = 2.33. \rightarrow -z_\alpha = -2.33$$

The critical region is:

$$R.C. = \frac{\dot{p} - \pi_0}{\sqrt{\pi_0(1 - \pi_0)/n}} < -2.33.$$

Exercise 21

Given a population with mean equal to 3.2, 81 samples are taken such that:

$$\sum_{i=1}^{81} x_i = 234.9 \quad \sum_{i=1}^{81} x_i^2 = 1001.21.$$

We want to test the null hypothesis:

$$H_0 : \mu = 3.2$$

Propose an unbiased estimator for the variance.

Calculate the confidence interval for the mean at the 0.9 level.
Test the hypothesis with significance levels of 0.1 and 0.05.

The unbiased estimator is the sample variance.
We have:

$$\bar{x} = \frac{1}{n} \sum_{i=1}^{81} x_i = 234.9/81 = 2.9,$$

$$S^2 = \frac{1}{n-1} \left[\sum_{i=1}^{n} X_i^2 - n\bar{X}^2 \right]$$

$$S^2 = \frac{1}{n-1} \left[\sum_{i=1}^{n} x_i^2 - n\bar{x}^2 \right] =$$

$$= \frac{1}{80} \left[1001.21 - 81 \times 2.9^2 \right]$$

$$= \frac{1}{80} (1001.21 - 681.21)$$

$$= \frac{1}{80} (320) = 4.$$

Since the number of samples is large, the central limit theorem can be used.
The required confidence interval is:

$$90\%CI = [l_1, l_2] \quad \left[\bar{x} - z_{\alpha/2} \frac{S}{\sqrt{n}}; \bar{x} + z_{\alpha/2} \frac{S}{\sqrt{n}} \right]$$

$$= \left[2.9 - 1.645\frac{2}{9}; 2.9 + 1.645\frac{2}{9} \right] = [2.535; 3.265].$$

The test statistic:

$$\frac{\bar{X} - \mu_0}{S/\sqrt{n}};$$

It is a normal standard.
Therefore,

$$P(T_n < t_n | \mu = 3.2) = P\left(\frac{\bar{X} - \mu_0}{S/\sqrt{n}} < \frac{2.9 - 3.2}{2/9}\right)$$
$$= P(Z < -1.35) = 1 - \Phi(1.35) = 0.09.$$

This result is in the critical region if the significance level is 0.1 but not 0.05.
Then, depending on the levels of significance, the null hypothesis will be rejected or accepted.

Exercise 22

Given a population of unknown mean and variance, 120 samples are extracted with mean equal to 25.3 and variance equal to 13'240.
Test the hypothesis that the mean is zero with a significance level of 1%.
Calculate the actual significance level.
Calculate the probability of error of the second type in the case of an alternative hypothesis with mean = 10.

The critical region is:

$$R.C. = \{z : z \geq z_\alpha\}.$$

$$R.C. = \{z : z \geq z_{0.99} = 2.326\}.$$

Since the number of samples is large, we can use the central limit theorem. Therefore:

$$t_n = \frac{(25.3 - 0)}{\sqrt{13240/120}} = 2.41$$

Falling back into the critical region, the null hypothesis has to be rejected. The actual significance level is:

$$p = P(\bar{X} \geq 25.3 | \mu = 0) = P\left(\frac{\bar{X} - \mu_0}{S/\sqrt{n}} \geq \frac{25.3 - 0}{\sqrt{13240/120}}\right)$$

$$= P(Z \geq 2.41) = 1 - 0.9920 = 0.008$$

Which is less than 1%, according to what we found earlier.
To determine the probability of a type II error, we have:

$$\frac{(\bar{x} - 0)}{\sqrt{13240/120}} \geq 2.326,$$

From which:

$$\bar{x}_c \geq 24.4.$$

So the critical region is:

$$R.C. = \{\bar{x} : \bar{x} \geq 24.4\}.$$

This probability is given by:

$$P(\bar{X} \in R.A. | H_1) = P(\bar{X} \leq 24.4 | \mu = 10) = P\left(\frac{\bar{X} - \mu_1}{S/\sqrt{n}} \leq \frac{24.4 - \mu_1}{S/\sqrt{n}}\right) =$$

$$= P\left(Z \leq \frac{24.4 - 10}{10.5}\right) = P(Z \leq 1.37) = 0.915.$$

Exercise 23

Given:

X N. unità	10	20	50	100	150	200
Y Costo unitario	9.4	9.2	9.0	8.5	8.1	7.4

Estimate correlation coefficient and say if it is adequate.
Estimate the parameters of the regression model.

The correlation coefficient is:

$$r_{XY} = \frac{\sum_{i=1}^{n}(x_i - \bar{x})(y_i - \bar{y})}{\sqrt{\sum_{i=1}^{n}(x_i - \bar{x})^2 \sum_{i=1}^{n}(y_i - \bar{y})^2}} =$$

$$= \frac{\sum_{i=1}^{n} x_i y_i - n\bar{x}\bar{y}}{\sqrt{(\sum_{i=1}^{n} x_i^2 - n\bar{x}^2)(\sum_{i=1}^{n} y_i^2 - n\bar{y}^2)}}$$

In our case we have:

$$\bar{x} = 530/6 = 88.\bar{3}$$
$$\bar{y} = 51.6/6 = 8.6$$

$$Dev(X) = \sum_{i=1}^{n}(x_i - \bar{x})^2 = 75500 - 6 \cdot 88.\bar{3}^2 = 28683.33$$

$$Dev(Y) = \sum_{i=1}^{n}(y_i - \bar{y})^2 = = 446.62 - 6 \cdot 8.6^2 = 2.86$$

$$Cod(X,Y) = \sum_{i=1}^{n}(x_i - \bar{x})(y_i - \bar{y}) = 4273 - n \cdot 88.3 \cdot 8.6 = -285$$

$$S_E^2 = \sum_{i=1}^{n} e_i^2$$

$$r_{XY} = -285/\sqrt{28683.33 \cdot 2.86} = -0.995$$

The relationship between the variables is not symmetric and therefore the correlation coefficient is inadequate. It is better to proceed with the regression analysis. Since:

$$S_E^2 = \sum_{i=1}^{n} e_i^2 = S_y^2 - \beta^2 S_x^2 = Dev(Y) - \beta^2 Dev(X)$$

We have:

$$\beta = Cod(X,Y)/Dev(X) = -285/28683.33 = -0.0099$$
$$\alpha = \bar{y} - \beta\bar{x} = 8.6 - (-0.0099) \cdot 88.\bar{3} = 9.4777$$
$$\hat{\sigma}^2 = \frac{Dev(Y) - \beta^2 Dev(X)}{n - 2} = (2.86 - (-0.0099)^2 \cdot 28683.33)/4 = 0.0071$$

Exercise 24

Data:

x_i	y_i
-2	2
-5	-3
4	10
5	8
8	20
10	60
-7	-18
12	24

Estimate the regression line and calculate the index of determination.
What is the most outlier?
By removing this value, estimate the new regression line and say whether
its index of determination explains more than 90% of the total variability.

We have:

$$\bar{y} = \frac{1}{n}\sum_i y_i = 12.875$$

$$\bar{x} = \frac{1}{n}\sum_i x_i = 3.125$$

$$S_y^2 = \frac{1}{n}\sum_i y_i^2 - \bar{y}^2 = \frac{1}{n}\sum_{i=1}^{n}(y_i - \bar{y})^2 = 468.8594$$

$$S_x^2 = \frac{1}{n}\sum_i x_i^2 - \bar{x}^2 = \frac{1}{n}\sum_{i=1}^{n}(x_i - \bar{x})^2 = 43.60938$$

$$S_{xy} = \frac{1}{n}\sum_i y_i x_i - \bar{y}\bar{x} = \frac{1}{n}\sum_{i=1}^{n}(x_i - \bar{x})(y_i - \bar{y}) = 117.8906$$

Therefore:

$$\hat{\beta} = \frac{S_{xy}}{S_x^2} =$$

$$= \frac{117.8906}{43.60938} = 2.703331$$

$$\hat{\alpha} = \bar{y} - \hat{\beta}\bar{x} =$$
$$= 12.875 - 2.703331 \cdot 3.125 = 4.427091.$$

And the line is:

$$\hat{y}_i = \hat{\alpha} + \hat{\beta}x_i = 4.427091 + 2.703331x_i$$

We know that:

$$Dev(Y) = n \cdot S_y^2 = 8 \cdot 468.8594 = 3750.8752$$
$$Dev(X) = n \cdot S_x^2 = 8 \cdot 43.60938 = 348.87504$$

$$\sum_{i=1}^{n} e_i^2 = Dev(Y) - \beta^2 Dev(X) = 3750.8752 - (2.703331)^2 348.87504 = 1201.296933$$

And so the index of determination is:

$$R^2 = \frac{\sum_{i=1}^{n}(\hat{y}_i - \bar{y}_i)^2}{\sum_{i=1}^{n}(y_i - \bar{y}_i)^2}$$

$$= 1 - \frac{\sum_{i=1}^{n} e_i^2}{\sum_{i=1}^{n}(y_i - \bar{y}_i)^2}$$

$$R^2 = 1 - \frac{1201.296933}{3750.8752} = 0.6797$$

From the observation of the residuals, it can be deduced that the sixth measurement is the most anomalous, having the largest residual.
By removing this measure:

$$\bar{y} \;=\; 6.142857$$
$$\bar{x} \;=\; 2.142857$$
$$S_y^2 \;=\; 173.2653$$
$$S_x^2 \;=\; 42.12245$$
$$S_{xy} \;=\; 81.83674$$

$$\hat{\beta} \;=\; \frac{S_{xy}}{S_x^2} \;=$$
$$=\; \frac{\frac{1}{n}\sum_i x_i y_i - \bar{y}\bar{x}}{\frac{1}{n}\sum_i x_i^2 - \bar{x}^2} \;=$$
$$=\; \frac{81.83674}{42.12245} \;=\; 1.942830$$

$$\hat{\alpha} \;=\; \bar{y} - \hat{\beta}\bar{x} \;=$$
$$=\; 6.142857 - 1.942830 \cdot 2.142857 = 1.97965.$$

The new correlation coefficient is:

$$r_{XY} \;=\; \frac{S_{xy}}{\sqrt{S_x^2 S_y^2}}$$
$$=\; \frac{81.83674}{\sqrt{42.12245 \cdot 173.2653}} \;=$$
$$=\; 0.9579343.$$

For which:

$$R^2 = 0.9579343^2 = 0.9176381 > 0.90.$$

And it explains more than 90%.

Exercise 25

Data:

$$\sum_{i=1}^{24} x_i = 42.8; \quad \sum_{i=1}^{24} y_i = 12.4;$$

$$\sum_{i=1}^{24} x_i^2 = 81.5; \quad \sum_{i=1}^{24} y_i^2 = 6.72, \quad \sum_{i=1}^{24} x_i y_i = 23.27$$

Calculate the regression line.

We have:

$$\bar{x} = \frac{1}{24}42.8 = 1.7833; \quad \bar{y} = \frac{1}{24}12.4 = 0.5167;$$

$$DEV(x) = \sum_{i=1}^{n} x_i^2 - n\bar{x}^2 = 81.5 - 76.3267 = 5.1733$$

$$\hat{\beta} = \frac{\sum_{i=1}^{n} x_i y_i - n\bar{x}\bar{y}}{\sum_{i=1}^{n} x_i^2 - n\bar{x}^2} = \frac{23.27 - 24 \cdot 1.7833 \cdot 0.5167}{5.1733} = 0.2236$$

$$\sum_{i=1}^{24}(y_i - \hat{\alpha} - \hat{\beta}x_i) = 0 \Rightarrow \hat{\alpha} = \bar{y} - \hat{\beta}\bar{x} = 0.1179$$

Exercise 26

Data:

x_i	y_i
1.6	10
2	15
3.5	20
3	21
3.2	24
4	30

Calculate the regression line and the index of determination.
We have:

	x_i	y_i	x_i^2	y_i^2	$x_i \cdot y_i$
	1.6	10	2.56	100	16
	2	15	4	225	30
	3.5	20	12.25	400	70
	3	21	9	441	63
	3.2	24	10.24	576	76.8
	4	30	16	900	120
Tot	17.3	120	54.05	2642	375.8
Tot/n	2.88333	20	9.00833	440.333	62.6333

And then:

$$\hat{\beta} = \frac{\sum_{i=1}^{n}(y_i - \bar{y})(x_i - \bar{x})}{\sum_{i=1}^{n}(x_i - \bar{x})^2} = \frac{n^{-1} \cdot \sum_{i=1}^{n} x_i y_i - \bar{x}\bar{y}}{n^{-1} \cdot \sum_{i=1}^{n} x_i^2 - \bar{x}^2} =$$
$$= \frac{62.6333 - 2.8833 \cdot 20}{9.0083 - 2.8833^2} = \frac{4.9673}{0.6947} =$$
$$= 7.15028$$

$$\hat{\alpha} = \bar{y} - \hat{\beta}\bar{x}$$
$$= 20 - 7.15028 \cdot 2.88333 = -0.6166168.$$

For the index of determination:

$$r_{XY} = \frac{S_{xy}}{\sqrt{S_x^2 \cdot S_y^2}}$$
$$= \frac{4.9667}{\sqrt{0.6947 \cdot (440.33 - 20^2)}} =$$
$$= \frac{4.9667}{\sqrt{0.6947 \cdot 40.333}} = 0.9382,$$

$$R^2 = r_{XY}^2 = 0.9382^2 = 0.8804$$

Exercise 27

Data:

$$\begin{aligned} \bar{y} &= 4 \\ \bar{x} &= 20 \\ S_y^2 &= 2 \\ S_x^2 &= 60 \\ \frac{1}{n}\sum_i x_i y_i &= 68 \end{aligned}$$

Estimate the parameters of a linear regression model.

We have:

$$\begin{aligned} \hat{\beta} &= \frac{S_{xy}}{S_x^2} = \\ &= \frac{\frac{1}{n}\sum_i x_i y_i - \bar{y}\cdot\bar{x}}{S_x^2} = \\ &= \frac{68 - 20\cdot 4}{60} = \frac{-12}{60} = -0.2 \\ \hat{\alpha} &= \bar{y} - \hat{\beta}\bar{x} = \\ &= 4 + 0.2\cdot 20 = 8. \end{aligned}$$

And then:

$$\begin{aligned} \hat{y}_{n+1} &= \hat{\alpha} + \hat{\beta}\cdot 22 \\ &= 8 - 0.2\cdot 22 = 3.6 \end{aligned}$$

47

STOCHASTIC PROCESSES

Definitions

A stochastic process represents a probabilistic dynamic system, i.e. a statistical evolution of a given system.

The variables of a stochastic process are obviously random variables, they are defined on a single finite sample space and assume values in a set called state space.

The characterization of a stochastic process takes place through the joint probability density function and thus it is possible to classify discrete and continuous stochastic processes.

If the transition probability between one state and the next depends on the previous states but not on time, we speak of a homogeneous stochastic process; cyclostationary stochastic processes, on the other hand, describe periodic phenomena and are particularly important in signal theory.

A Gaussian stochastic process is a stochastic process whose random variables have joint probability distribution given by a Gaussian.

A Gaussian process is identified by its expected value and variance, as is a Gaussian function.

In signal theory, a Gaussian process defined over time is Gaussian noise (also called white noise).

A stochastic process whose transition probability depends only on the starting state is said to be Markovian.

A Markov process has the Markov property (also called no-memory):

$$\forall h > 0, t > 0$$

$$\Downarrow$$

$$\Pr\left[X(t+h) = y \mid X(s) = x(s), s \leq t\right] = \Pr\left[X(t+h) = y \mid X(t) = x(t)\right]$$

If the Markov property does not depend on time, we have homogeneous Markov processes:

$\forall h > 0, \forall t$

$\Downarrow$

$$\Pr\big[X(t+h) = y \mid X(t) = x(t)\big] = \Pr\big[X(h) = y \mid X(0) = x(0)\big]$$

If a process is not Markov, it is always possible to construct Markov processes of second order, or of higher order, by taking a reference time interval of that process.

Markov chains and other processes

A Markov chain is a Markov process having a discrete state space.
This chain can be continuous in time or discrete in time based on how the variable given by time is considered.
In a homogeneous Markov chain, the transition probability between states depends only on the distance of the time instants and not on the absolute value of time.
A homogeneous finite-state Markov chain is represented by a transition matrix of states and an initial probability vector.
The transition matrix has all elements greater than or equal to zero (due to the properties of probabilities) and also the sum of the elements on a row is equal to one.
A discrete-state Markov chain is said to be periodic if, after a number of time steps, there is a non-zero probability of returning to the initial state of the period.
A discrete-state Markov chain is said to be irreducible if starting from each state there is a non-zero probability of reaching every other state.
A stationary probability distribution of a discrete-state homogeneous Markov chain is a discrete probability distribution that remains constant even as the Markov chain evolves over time.
If the Markov chain is irreducible, such a distribution exists and is unique.
If the chain is also aperiodic, the probability distribution at the nth step converges to the stationary distribution, regardless of the initial choice of the probability distribution.
Ergodic Markov chains are based on ergodic theory, itself descended from the ergodic theorem.
This theorem states that a conservative transformation for the measure over a measurable space has a time mean and a space mean which coincide almost everywhere.
The time average is calculated on a function that can be integrated on L^1 and the transformation thus defined is called ergodic.

In an ergodic Markov chain, the probability at any instant and for any initial condition exists and is independent of time and initial conditions.
A hidden Markov model is a Markov chain in which the states are not observable, but only the events are.

A stochastic Bernoulli process is a discrete process of independent random variables which are characterized by Bernoulli's law.
Also in this process there is a lack of memory.
Given, for each random variable, the probability of success p (and that of failure given by 1-p), the number of successes after n trials follows the binomial law B(p,n), while the number of trials to obtain a success follows the geometric law of ratio equal to 1-p.

A stochastic Poisson process is a process that generalizes the Bernoulli process to the continuum.
It is also an example of a continuous-time Markov chain.
The increments are stationary, i.e. they depend only on the length of the time interval considered and have a Poisson distribution equal to:

$$\forall k \in N \Rightarrow P(N_{t+\tau} - N_t = k) = \frac{e^{-\lambda\tau}(\lambda\tau)^k}{k!}$$

At the nth time, the event follows the gamma distribution with parameters given by n and the inverse of the intensity.
If only one event has occurred in a certain time interval, then the Poisson process has a uniform distribution.
Given two independent Poisson processes, their sum is still a Poisson process given by the sum of the intensities of the individual processes.
A compound Poisson process is a continuous time process on the set of natural numbers whose "jumps" between one number and another are defined by a law related to a Poisson process.
In particular we have, for any t>0:

$$Y(t) = \sum_{i=1}^{N(t)} D_i$$

Where N(t) is a Poisson process and D are the independent random variables defined on the set of natural numbers. The expected value and the variance are defined as follows:

$$E(Y(t)) = \lambda t E(D)$$

$$Var(Y(t)) = \lambda t E(D^2)$$

A Lévy process is a continuous stochastic process with stationary and independent increments. At time zero, the process is almost certainly null. A Poisson process is a particular Lévy process.

A Markov chain whose transitions are given by random variables is called a random walk.
This process can be seen as a discretization of a Lévy process.
In the one-dimensional random walk, the random variable that provides the number of steps in one direction after N movements is a discrete variable with a binomial distribution.
The probability of returning to the origin tends to the certain event for a number of movements which tends to infinity.
For the two-dimensional case, two stochastically independent binomial random variables are defined, while for the three-dimensional case the variables become three.
The transition to the continuum of a random walk leads to a Lévy process whose increments are given by random variables.
This process is a model for Brownian motion which is an important result of statistical physics applied to classical mechanics.

A Wiener process is a Lévy process, which is also Gaussian, used to model Brownian motion.
The time intervals of such a process are represented by a Gaussian distribution of mean date and variance.
It is also possible to define a Wiener measure, that is a probability law induced by the Wiener process on the space of continuous functions and associate an integral, called Wiener's, to this measure.
Furthermore, the differential of a Wiener process can also be defined as that process which has the mean quadratic coincident with the differential of the quadratic mean of the starting Wiener process:

$$E(dW_t^2) = dE(W_t^2)$$

Having defined the differential of the process in this way:

$$dW_t = N \sqrt{dt}$$

Exercises

Exercise 1

Let N be a process with independent increments with:

$$\mu_0 = \delta_0 \text{ e } \mu_{s,t} = Po(\lambda(t-s)).$$

Verify that:

$$\mu_{s,u} = \mu_{s,t} * \mu_{t,u}.$$

To calculate:

$$\mathbb{E}[|N_t - N_s|^{\beta}]$$

For beta equal to 1, 2 and 3.

The sum of two independent Poisson random variables is a parameter random variable equal to the sum of the parameters. Then the convolution is immediately verified.
We have:

$$\varphi_{X_t - X_s}(u) = \varphi(u) = \exp\left(\lambda(t-s)(e^{iu} - 1)\right)$$

And then:

$$
\begin{aligned}
\varphi'(u) &= \lambda(t-s)ie^{iu}\varphi(u), \\
\varphi''(u) &= \left(-\lambda(t-s)e^{iu} - \lambda^2(t-s)^2 e^{2iu}\right)\varphi(u), \\
\varphi'''(u) &= \left(-i\lambda(t-s)e^{iu} - 3i\lambda^2(t-s)^2 e^{2iu} - i\lambda^3(t-s)^3 e^{3iu}\right)\varphi(u),
\end{aligned}
$$

From which:

$$
\begin{aligned}
\mathbb{E}[|N_t - N_s|] &= \mathbb{E}[N_t - N_s] = -i\varphi'(0) = \lambda(t-s), \\
\mathbb{E}[|N_t - N_s|^2] &= \mathbb{E}[(N_t - N_s)^2] = -\varphi''(0) = \lambda(t-s) + \lambda^2(t-s)^2, \\
\mathbb{E}[|N_t - N_s|^3] &= \mathbb{E}[(N_t - N_s)^3] = i\varphi'''(0) = \lambda(t-s) + 3\lambda^2(t-s)^2 + \lambda^3(t-s)^3
\end{aligned}
$$

Exercise 2

Let B be a Brownian motion.
Prove that the following processes are also Brownian motions:

$$X_t := B_{t+s} - B_s \text{ per } s > 0;$$

$$X_t := -B_t;$$

$$X_t := cB_{t/c^2} \text{ per } c \in \mathbb{R}^*;$$

$$X_t := tB_{1/t}1_{\{t>0\}};$$

For the first case we have:

$$X_0 = B_s - B_s = 0,$$
$$X_u - X_t = B_{u+s} - B_s - B_{t+s} + B_s = B_{u+s} - B_{t+s}$$
$$X_u - X_t = B_{u+s} - B_{t+s} \sim N(0, u+s-t-s) = N(0, u-t),$$

For the second case:

$$X_0 = -B_0 = 0,$$
$$X_t - X_s = -B_t + B_s$$
$$X_t - X_s = -B_t + B_s \sim N(0, t-s)$$

For the third case:

$$X_0 = B_0 = 0,$$
$$X_t - X_s = c(B_{t/c^2} - B_{s/c^2})$$

$$X_t - X_s = c(B_{t/c^2} - B_{s/c^2}) \sim N\left(0, c^2\left(\frac{t}{c^2} - \frac{s}{c^2}\right)\right) = N(0, t-s)$$

For the fourth case, time is reversed, so we have to proceed differently.

$$X_0 = 0.$$
$$(X_{t_1}, \ldots, X_{t_n}) = (t_1 B_{1/t_1}, \ldots, t_n B_{1/t_n})$$

The latter is a Gaussian random vector and we have:

$$\mathbb{E}[X_s X_t] = \mathbb{E}[s B_{1/s} t B_{1/t}] = st\mathbb{E}[B_{1/s} B_{1/t}] = st\frac{1}{t} = s$$

Hence the thesis.

Exercise 3

Given n Brownian motions independent of each other and composed so as to form an n-dimensional Brownian motion, called A the finite and positive Lebesgue measure, let be:

$$S_A(\omega) := \{t \in \mathbb{R}^+ \mid B_t(\omega) \in A\}$$

For t>0, what reads and what density does the random vector B(t) have? Calling lambda the Lebesgue measure, show that:

$$\mathbb{E}[\lambda(S_A)] = \begin{cases} +\infty & \text{se } m \leq 2, \\[2ex] \dfrac{1}{2\pi^{m/2}}\Gamma\left(\dfrac{m}{2} - 1\right) \displaystyle\int_A \|x\|^{2-m}\, dx & \text{se } m > 2. \end{cases}$$

Since the components of B(t) are centered Gaussians with variance t, we have that the distribution of B(t) is normal (0,tI) where I is the n-dimensional identity matrix.
The density is then:

$$f(x) = \frac{1}{\sqrt{(2\pi t)^d}} e^{-\frac{1}{2t}\|x\|^2}$$

Applying Tonelli's theorem:

$$\mathbb{E}[\lambda(S_A)] = \mathbb{E}\left[\int_0^\infty 1_{\{B_t \in A\}}\, dt\right] = \int_0^\infty \mathbb{P}\{B_t \in A\}\, dt = \int_0^\infty \int_A (2\pi t)^{-\frac{d}{2}} e^{-\frac{1}{2t}\|x\|^2}\, dx\, dt$$

Reversing the order of integration and setting:

$$u := \frac{\|x\|^2}{t}$$

We have:

$$
\begin{aligned}
\mathbb{E}[\lambda(S_A)] &= \int_A \int_0^\infty (2\pi)^{-\frac{d}{2}} \left(\frac{\|x\|^2}{u}\right)^{-\frac{d}{2}} e^{-\frac{1}{2}u} \frac{\|x\|^2}{u^2}\, du\, dx = \\
&= \int_A \|x\|^{2-d}\, dx \int_0^\infty (2\pi)^{-\frac{d}{2}} u^{\frac{d}{2}-2} e^{-\frac{1}{2}u}\, du
\end{aligned}
$$

The integral is bounded only if d>2 and holds:

$$\frac{\Gamma(\frac{d}{2} - 1)}{(\frac{1}{2})^{\frac{d}{2}-1}} = 2^{\frac{d}{2}-1}\Gamma\left(\frac{d}{2} - 1\right)$$

Exercise 4

Let B be a Brownian motion with respect to a filtration such that:

$$\mathcal{F}_\infty := \bigvee_t \mathcal{F}_t.$$

And let G be an independent sigma-algebra with:

$$\tilde{\mathcal{F}}_t := \mathcal{F}_t \vee \mathcal{G}, \; t \geq 0.$$

Prove that B is a Brownian motion also in this filtration.

We have:

$$B_0 = 0$$
$$B_t - B_s \sim N(0, t - s)$$

Just show that:

$$B_t - B_s$$

It is independent of:

$$A \cup B, \text{ con } A \in \mathcal{F}_s \text{ e } B \in \mathcal{G}$$

We immediately see that the quantity demanded is independent of B.
From the logical properties it will also be independent of:

$$A \cup B = (A^c \cap B^c)^c$$

Hence the thesis.

Exercise 5

Given two random variables X and Y with values in E and G and a sigma-algebra contained in F such that X is measurable and Y independent.
Prove that for every measurable and bounded function:

$$\mathbb{E}[f(X, Y) \mid \mathcal{F}'] = h(X)$$

$$h(x) := \mathbb{E}[f(x, Y)].$$

From the definition of expected value:

$$\mathbb{E}[f(X,Y)\mid\mathcal{F}'] = \mathbb{E}[1_A(X)1_B(Y)\mid\mathcal{F}'] = 1_A(X)\mathbb{E}[1_B(Y)\mid\mathcal{F}'] = 1_A(X)\mathbb{P}\{Y\in B\}$$

And then:

$$h(x) = \mathbb{E}[f(x,Y)] = \mathbb{E}[1_A(x)1_B(Y)] = 1_A(x)\mathbb{P}\{Y\in B\}$$

Exercise 6

Given a Brownian motion B with respect to a filtration F and a Gaussian variable independent of B.
Place:

$$Y_t := \eta t + \sigma B_t$$

$$\mathcal{G}_t := \sigma(Y_s | S \le t).$$

Calculate for s<t:

$$\mathrm{Cov}\,(\eta, Y_s)\ \mathrm{e}\ \mathrm{Cov}\,(Y_s, Y_t)$$

The covariances are calculated from the definition:

$$\mathrm{Cov}\,(\eta, Y_s) = \mathrm{Cov}\,(\eta, \eta s + \sigma B_s) = s\mathrm{Var}\,[\eta] = s\rho^2$$

$$\mathrm{Cov}\,(Y_s, Y_t) = \mathrm{Cov}\,(\eta s + \sigma B_s, \eta t + \sigma B_t)$$
$$= st\mathrm{Var}\,[\eta] + \sigma^2\mathrm{Cov}\,(B_s, B_t) = st\rho^2 + s\sigma^2$$

Exercise 7

Let G be a sub-sigma-algebra of F and X a random vector such that for each lambda:

$$\mathbb{E}[e^{i\langle\lambda,X\rangle} \mid \mathcal{G}] = \mathbb{E}[e^{i\langle\lambda,X\rangle}]$$

Prove that X is independent of G.

It suffices to show that X is independent of any G-measurable random variable Y.
The characteristic function of (X,Y) is given by:

$$\varphi_{(X,Y)}(\lambda,t) = \mathbb{E}[e^{i\langle\lambda,X\rangle+itY}] = \mathbb{E}[\mathbb{E}[e^{i\langle\lambda,X\rangle+itY} \mid \mathcal{G}]] = \mathbb{E}[e^{itY}\mathbb{E}[e^{i\langle\lambda,X\rangle} \mid \mathcal{G}]] =$$
$$= \mathbb{E}[e^{itY}\mathbb{E}[e^{i\langle\lambda,X\rangle}]] = \mathbb{E}[e^{itY}]\mathbb{E}[e^{i\langle\lambda,X\rangle}] = \varphi_X(\lambda)\varphi_Y(t)$$

From which follows independence.

Exercise 8

Given an integrable square martingale, prove that, for each s<t we have:

$$\mathbb{E}[(M_t - M_s)^2] = \mathbb{E}[M_t^2] - \mathbb{E}[M_s^2]$$

Also, if it is independently incrementing, show that its quadratic variance is:

$$\langle M\rangle_t = \mathbb{E}[(M_t - M_0)^2] = \mathbb{E}[M_t^2] - \mathbb{E}[M_0^2]$$

Applying the definition, we have:

$$\mathbb{E}[(M_t - M_s)^2] = \mathbb{E}[\mathbb{E}[M_t^2 - 2M_tM_s + M_s^2 \mid \mathcal{F}_s]] :$$
$$= \mathbb{E}[\mathbb{E}[M_t^2 \mid \mathcal{F}_s] - 2M_s^2 + M_s^2] = \mathbb{E}[M_t^2] - \mathbb{E}[M_s^2]$$

We verify that this quantity is a martingale:

$$(M_t^2 - \mathbb{E}[(M_t - M_0)^2])_t$$

We have:

$$\mathbb{E}[M_t^2 - \mathbb{E}[(M_t - M_s)^2]|\mathcal{F}_s] = \mathbb{E}[(M_t - M_s + M_s)^2 - \mathbb{E}[(M_t - M_s)^2]|\mathcal{F}_s] =$$
$$= \mathbb{E}[(M_t - M_s)^2] + 2M_s\mathbb{E}[M_t - M_s] + M_s^2 - \mathbb{E}[(M_t - M_0)^2] =$$
$$= \mathbb{E}[M_t^2] - \mathbb{E}[M_s^2] + M_s^2 - \mathbb{E}[M_t^2] + \mathbb{E}[M_0^2] = M_s^2 - \mathbb{E}[(M_s - M_0)^2]$$

Exercise 9

Given a continuous and non-negative martingale, such that:

$$M_0 = 1$$
$$\lim_{t \to +\infty} M_t = 0$$

Given a>1, we define the first time of passage for a as:

$$\tau_a := \inf\{t \mid M_t \geq a\}$$

Prove that:

$$\lim_{t \to +\infty} M_{t \wedge \tau_a} = a1_{\{\tau_a < +\infty\}}.$$

Given the event:

$$\{\tau_a < +\infty\}$$

We have:

$$M_{t \wedge \tau_a} \to M_\tau = a$$

Considered instead:

$$\{\tau_a = +\infty\}$$

You get:

$$M_{t \wedge \tau_a} \longrightarrow \lim_{t \to +\infty} M_t = 0$$

Combining the two results we get the thesis.

Exercise 10

Given a Brownian motion, a and b positive, we define the exit time of B from the interval [-a,b] as:

$$\tau := \inf\{t \mid B_t \notin [-a, b]\}$$

Show that this time is not infinite.
Also calculate:

$$\mathbb{P}\{B_\tau = -a\}$$
$$\mathbb{P}\{B_\tau = b\}.$$

How the problem was posed:

$$\limsup_{t \to +\infty} B_t = +\infty$$
$$\liminf_{t \to +\infty} B_t = -\infty$$

It follows that time is not infinite.
Since B is a martingale, so is:

$$(B_{t \wedge \tau})_t$$

And then:

$$\mathbb{E}[B_{t \wedge \tau}] = \mathbb{E}[B_0] = 0.$$

But:

$$B_{t \wedge \tau} \longrightarrow B_\tau$$
$$|B_{t \wedge \tau}| \le \max(a, b) \in L^1(\Omega, \mathcal{F}, \mathbb{P};$$

Combining the results we get:

$$0 = \lim_{t \to +\infty} \mathbb{E}[B_{t \wedge \tau}] = \mathbb{E}[B_\tau] = b\mathbb{P}\{B_\tau = b\} - a\mathbb{P}\{B_\tau = -a\}$$

This should be done with:

$$\mathbb{P}\{B_\tau = -a\} + \mathbb{P}\{B_\tau = b\} = 1$$

The solutions are:

$$\mathbb{P}\{B_\tau = -a\} = \frac{b}{a+b}$$

$$\mathbb{P}\{B_\tau = b\} = \frac{a}{a+b}$$

Exercise 11

Given a probability space and a filtration, let us consider two measures P and Q such that, for each t>0, the restriction of Q is absolutely continuous with respect to the analogous restriction of P and of density equal to:

$$Z_t := \frac{d\mathbb{Q}|_{\mathcal{F}_t}}{d\mathbb{P}|_{\mathcal{F}_t}}$$

Prove that Z is a martingale with respect to P.

We simply have that:

$$\mathbb{E}_{\mathbb{P}}[Z_t 1_A] = \mathbb{Q}(A) = \mathbb{E}_{\mathbb{P}}[Z_s 1_A]$$

This implies that:

$$\mathbb{E}[Z_t | \mathcal{F}_s] = Z_s.$$

And so Z is a martingale.

Exercise 12

Given a probability space and defined as a sequence of independent random variables with zero mean and definite variance, we define the random walk as:

$$S_0 := 0, \qquad S_n := X_1 + \ldots + X_n \quad \text{per } n \in \mathbb{N},$$

Place:

$$Z_0 := 0, \qquad Z_n := \frac{S_n^2}{\sqrt{n}} \quad \text{per } n \in \mathbb{N}.$$

$$\eta_k := Z_k - Z_{k-1}.$$

$$Z_n = \sum_{k=1}^n \eta_k.$$

$$\eta_k = \begin{cases} S_1^2 & \text{se } k = 1 \\ \dfrac{S_k^2}{\sqrt{k}} - \dfrac{S_{k-1}^2}{\sqrt{k-1}} & \text{se } k \geq 2 \end{cases}.$$

Show that:

$$E(\eta_n | \mathcal{F}_{n-1}) \leq \frac{\sigma^2}{\sqrt{n}}.$$

Also show that the process

$$Y = \{Y_n := Z_n - g(n)\}_{n \in \mathbb{N}_0}$$

$$g(0) := 0, \qquad g(n) := \sum_{k=1}^{n} \frac{\sigma^2}{\sqrt{k}} \quad \text{per } n \in \mathbb{N}.$$

It's a martingale.

For n=1 we have:

$$E(\eta_1 | \mathcal{F}_0) = E(\eta_1) = E(S_1^2) = \sigma^2$$

For n greater than or equal to 2:

$$S_n^2 = (S_{n-1} + X_n)^2 = S_{n-1}^2 + X_n^2 + 2 S_{n-1} X_n$$

And then:

$$E(S_n^2 | \mathcal{F}_{n-1}) = S_{n-1}^2 + E(X_n^2) = S_{n-1}^2 + \sigma^2$$

We obtain that:

$$E(\eta_n | \mathcal{F}_{n-1}) = \frac{E(S_n^2 | \mathcal{F}_{n-1})}{\sqrt{n}} - \frac{S_{n-1}^2}{\sqrt{n-1}} = \frac{\sigma^2}{\sqrt{n}} + S_{n-1}^2 \left(\frac{1}{\sqrt{n}} - \frac{1}{\sqrt{n-1}} \right) \leq \frac{\sigma^2}{\sqrt{n}}.$$

Furthermore, given that:

$$Z_n - Z_{n-1} = \eta_n.$$

We have:

$$E(Y_n | \mathcal{F}_{n-1}) = E(Z_n | \mathcal{F}_{n-1}) - g(n) =$$

$$E(\eta_n | \mathcal{F}_{n-1}) + Z_{n-1} - \sum_{k=1}^{n} \frac{\sigma^2}{\sqrt{k}} \leq Z_{n-1} - \sum_{k=1}^{n-1} \frac{\sigma^2}{\sqrt{k}} = Y_{n-1}$$

That is, Y is a martingale.

Exercise 13

On a standard filtered probability space a real Brownian motion is defined. Given two positive numbers a and b, we fix the stopping time as:

$$\tau := \inf\{t \in [0, \infty) : \ B_t \notin (-a, b)\}.$$

With the following properties:

$$P(B_\tau = -a) = \frac{b}{a + b}, \qquad P(B_\tau = b) = \frac{a}{a + b}, \qquad E(\tau) = ab \ (< \infty).$$

Prove that:

$$E(B_\tau^3) = ab(b - a).$$
$$E(\tau B_\tau 1_{\{B_\tau = -a\}}) = a\,E(\tau 1_{\{B_\tau = b\}}) - a^2 b.$$

Assuming the following identity:

$$1 = 1_{\{B_\tau = -a\}} + 1_{\{B_\tau = b\}}$$

It is obtained:

$$E(B_\tau^3) = E(B_\tau^3 1_{\{B_\tau = -a\}}) + E(B_\tau^3 1_{\{B_\tau = b\}}) =$$
$$(-a)^3 P(B_\tau = -a) + b^3 P(B_\tau = b)$$
$$= -\frac{a^3 b}{a + b} + \frac{b^3 a}{a + b} = ab\frac{b^2 - a^2}{b + a} = ab(b - a)$$

Moreover:

$$E(\tau 1_{\{B_\tau = -a\}}) + E(\tau 1_{\{B_\tau = b\}}) = E(\tau) = ab.$$

$$E(\tau B_\tau 1_{\{B_\tau = -a\}}) = -a\,E(\tau 1_{\{B_\tau = -a\}}) =$$

$$-a(ab - \mathrm{E}(\tau 1_{\{B_\tau = b\}})) = a\,\mathrm{E}(\tau 1_{\{B_\tau = b\}}) - a^2 b.$$

Exercise 14

Given n independent real random variables Z defined on a probability space with marginal laws given by the standard normal and given a sequence of positive numbers t with summable square, we have:

$$X_0 := 0$$

$$X_n := \sum_{i=1}^{n} t_i Z_i, \qquad \forall n \in \mathbb{N}.$$

Show that the process is a martingale and compute:

$$\mathrm{E}(X_n^2)_!$$

Deducing the necessary convergences.

By placing:

$$\mathcal{F}_0 := \{\emptyset, \Omega\}$$
$$\mathcal{F}_n := \sigma(Z_1, \ldots, Z_n)$$

The process is a martingale by definition itself. We have:
$$X_n \sim \mathcal{N}(0, t_1^2 + \ldots + t_n^2)$$
$$\mathrm{E}(X_n^2) = t_1^2 + \ldots + t_n^2.$$

This sum is limited by hypothesis. So the martingale is bounded L^2 by convergences:

$$X_n \to X_\infty$$
$$X_\infty < \infty$$

Exercise 15

A real Brownian motion B is defined on a standard filtered probability space. Given an arbitrary strictly increasing sequence of numbers t, let us say:

$$t_0 := 0$$

$$Y_i := B_{t_i} - B_{t_{i-1}}, \qquad \forall i \in \mathbb{N}.$$

Prove that:

$$P(Y_1 > 0, \ldots, Y_n > 0) = \frac{1}{2^n}.$$

$$P(B_{t_n} > B_{t_{n-1}} > \ldots > B_{t_2} > B_{t_1} > B_{t_0}) = \frac{1}{2^n}.$$

The variables Y are independent and with symmetric laws given by the normals with zero mean, therefore we have:

$$P(Y_1 > 0, \ldots, Y_n > 0) = P(Y_1 > 0) \cdots P(Y_n > 0) = \tfrac{1}{2^n}$$

We note that the events:

$$\{B_{t_n} > B_{t_{n-1}} > \ldots > B_{t_2} > B_{t_1} > B_{t_0}\}$$
$$\{Y_1 > 0, \ldots, Y_n > 0\}$$

They coincide and therefore the result follows accordingly.

48

ADVANCED ALGEBRA

Introduction and definitions

Advanced algebra includes abstract algebra, i.e. the study of algebraic structures, such as groups, rings and fields, category theory which tends to abstract individual algebraic structures, universal algebra which studies the common bases of all algebraic structures and the various types of algebra that can be constructed.

Referring to the next chapter for the study of algebraic structures and category theory, universal algebra defines algebra as a set A endowed with a set of operations on A.

An n-ary operation on A is a function that relates n elements of A to a single element of A.

A nullary operation is simply a constant, a unary operation is a function that relates A to A.

A binary operation is said to have arity equal to two, i.e. it is a function of the Cartesian product AxA which refers to A.

A binary operation is also called law of composition and an algebraic structure with a binary operation is called magma, the simplest algebraic structure.

Other more complex algebraic structures are defined by two or more binary operations.

Sum and product are examples of two binary operations, while subtraction is not if it refers to the set of natural numbers.

Operations with higher arity can also be infinite operations.

Each operation can be subject to different axioms, among which we recall the properties of associativity, distributivity, existence of the identity element, of the neutral one or of the inverse one.

Types of algebra

A graded algebra is an algebra defined on particular structures, such as a field or a commutative ring.

Linear algebra is the algebra underlying linear systems, vector spaces, matrix mathematics, and analytic geometry.

The algebra related to combinatorics, with the definition of probability and related properties, is called sigma-algebra and is the typical algebra defined on sets.

The study of algorithms and information and recursive structures is called computational algebra.

An algebra in which the internal unary operation is given by the normal derivative is called a differential algebra.

An algebra involving elementary logical operators and truth tables is called Boolean algebra.

An algebra on a field K is called K-algebra and is thus defined as a vector space A on the field K endowed with a binary operation which is a bilinear form, ie which satisfies the properties of bilinear distributivity and bilinear associativity of a scalar.

K is called the base field of algebra A and the binary operation is called product, although in reality it is not always the usual product operation.

Two algebras defined on the same field are said to be isomorphic if and only if there is a bijective linear map connecting them.

Every K-algebra can be specified up to isomorphisms by giving an n-th dimension and specifying the n structure coefficients.

We define commutative algebra as that part of abstract algebra which studies commutative algebraic structures, in the same way a non-commutative algebra deals with non-commutative algebraic structures.

With similar concepts one can define an associative algebra.

Examples of associative algebras are given of the algebra of square matrices defined on a field (and with the product operation given by the normal multiplication between matrices), the algebra (which is also commutative) of all polynomials on the field K.

An associative algebra over real numbers or complex numbers that is also a Banach space is called a Banach algebra.

The product operation defined on this algebra is a continuous function, furthermore the algebra is normed if the space is normed.

A Banach algebra is said to be unitary if it has an identity element for the product operation whose norm is equal to one and is said to be commutative if the product is commutative.

The set of real numbers and that of complex numbers are Banach algebras if the norm of the absolute value is defined, in the same way the sets of real or complex square matrices are Banach algebras by associating a norm to these matrices.

A Banach algebra on a complex field endowed with an involution property which sends an element into its conjugate and which enjoys this property:

$$\forall x \in A \implies \left\| x^* x \right\| = \left\| x \right\|^2$$

It's called C^* algebra.

Given two C^* algebras, an algebraic homomorphism is a homomorphism which respects the involution property.
The algebra of square matrices over a complex field becomes an C^* algebra if it has the classical norm.

If an C^* algebra admits an algebraic tensor product with any other C^* algebra, then it is said to be nuclear.

A generalization of an C^* algebra is given by B^* algebra: in fact in this case the involution operation respects the properties of associativity, isometry and anti-commutativity.
An associative algebra having a quadratic form Q on a vector space V is called Clifford algebra Cl(V,Q).
Once an nth basis of the space V is defined, the dimension of the Clifford algebra is equal to:

$$\dim Cl(V,Q) = 2^n$$

A not necessarily associative algebra whose product is commutative and satisfies the following Jordan identity is called a Jordan algebra:

$$(xy)(xx) = x(y(xx))$$

Given any associative algebra, but not one with characteristic equal to two, a Jordan algebra can be defined simply by using the addition operation in the vector space.

An associative algebra defined for any partially ordered set is called an incidence algebra.
The identity element for the product of an incidence algebra is the Kronecker delta, while the zeta function is the unit constant.

A Lie algebra defined on a vector space and on a field has a binary operator called the Lie product which is bilinear, antisymmetric, nilpotent and satisfies the Jacobi identity:

$$\left[\left[x, y\right], z\right] + \left[\left[z, x\right], y\right] + \left[\left[y, z\right], x\right] = 0$$

A Lie algebra is said to be Abelian if the Lie product yields the zero vector for all x and y.
The three-dimensional Euclidean space with the classical vector product is a Lie algebra.
An associative algebra can be transformed into a Lie algebra by defining the Lie product as the commutator:

$$\left[x, y\right] = xy - yx$$

Vector field algebras defined on differentiable manifolds are Lie algebras. A complex Lie algebra defined as an extension of the vector field of complex polynomials on the unit circle is called a Virasoro algebra.

An algebra over a field for which the product is alternative is called an alternative algebra. The alternative product is defined as follows:

$$(xx)y = x(xy)$$
$$y(xx) = (yx)x$$

Every associative algebra is alternative, but the opposite is not necessarily the case.

We define associative algebras on powers algebras for which the following product relations hold:

$$\forall m, n \in N \Rightarrow x^m * x^n = x^{m-n}$$

Of particular importance is the sequence of Caylery-Dickson algebras on real fields.
We can include the dimensional algebra of complexes (which is commutative and associative), the algebra of quaternions which is associative, that of octonions which is alternative and that of sedenions which is associative over powers.
We will define in the next chapter the algebraic structures related to these important objects of advanced mathematics.

An algebra is of division if there are multiplicative inverses while it is quadratic if the decomposition of the square according to the sum of elements of the base field and of the invertible element holds.

Up to isomorphisms, the only quadratic algebras on the reals are the real numbers, the complex ones, the quaternions and the octonions.

An algebra with two products involving a commutative algebra and a Lie algebra is called a Poisson algebra.

Given a topological space (X,T), the Borel algebra of X with respect to T is the smallest sigma-algebra containing the topology T.

Given two topological spaces and a continuous function connecting them, then this function is said to be measurable with respect to the Borel algebra.

The measurable functions in this algebra are called Borel's, as are the sets (sometimes also called Borel's) and the measure is precisely that of Borel.

Two borelian spaces are isomorphic if there exists a measurable bijective function with an inverse that is also measurable.

The most used Borel algebra is the one defined on real numbers and Euclidean spaces, in particular as regards the definition of probability.

A superalgebra over a commutative ring or field K is a direct-sum decomposition with bilinear multiplication such that we have:

$$A = A_0 \oplus A_1 \mid A \times A \rightarrow A \mid A_i A_j \subseteq A_{i+j}$$

In theoretical physics, we define supersymmetric algebras, i.e. those that incorporate the concept of supersymmetry between particles.

There are supersymmetric extensions of both the Lie algebra and the Virasoro algebra.

Similarly, there are supercommutative algebras which extend the concept of commutator.

Noteworthy is the Poincaré superalgebra, a supersymmetric extension of the Poincaré algebra, itself defined as the Lie algebra of the Poincaré group.

49

ALGEBRAIC STRUCTURES

Introduction and definitions

A mathematical structure defined on a set consists of objects that characterize the set, such as measure, topology, metrics, ordering, and algebra.

An algebraic structure is a support set of the structure endowed with operations that can be nullary, unary and binary and which have specific properties.

In this chapter we will give a detailed list of the main algebraic structures and their properties.

We define substructure as a subset of an algebraic structure which is closed under the operations defined in it.

A class is a generic collection of objects that can be identified.

All sets are classes, while classes that are not sets are called proper classes.

A morphism is a process that transforms one structure into another while keeping some of its properties unchanged.

Each morphism starts from a domain and connects it to a codomain, furthermore for each object there is a morphism called identity which transforms a structure into itself by means of composition with the same morphism.

A homomorphism is an application between two algebraic structures of the same type which preserves the operations defined therein.

An injective homomorphism is called a monomorphism, a surjective one is called an epimorphism, and a bijective one is called an isomorphism.

If the domain and the codomain coincide, then every homomorphism is called an endomorphism (an example is given by the identity function) and every isomorphism is called an automorphism.

If a domain has ordering properties, then there exists an order isomorphism, called isotonia, which maintains the ordering property also in the codomain.

We will see that particular isomorphisms can be defined in every algebraic structure, for now we recall that an isomorphism between vector spaces is a bijective linear transformation and one between topological spaces is a bijective map called homeomorphism.

An automorphism of a set is a permutation of the elements of the set; an automorphism of a vector space is an invertible linear operator on the space.

We can distinguish internal automorphisms deriving from conjugations between elements of the same object and external automorphisms.

Category theory and Euler characteristic

The study of morphisms and classes is done in detail in category theory.

By category we mean a mathematical entity endowed with a class Ob(C) whose elements are called objects, with a class Mor(C) whose elements are called morphisms and with a binary operation, called composition of morphisms, which satisfies the property association and the existence of identity.

A category is said to be small if the object class is a set.

Categories are sets, functions, homomorphisms, vector spaces, measurable spaces, topological spaces and differentiable manifolds.

The maps between the categories that preserve their structures are called functors.

Within the functors, one can distinguish the covariant ones from the contravariant ones.

The Euler characteristic is an integer describing the nature of the algebraic structure. It was initially introduced for polyhedra like this:

$$\chi = V - S + F$$

Where V, S and F are the number of vertices, edges and faces of the polyhedron.

For all simply connected polyhedra this value is equal to 2.

The concept can be extended to topological spaces and algebraic structures by recalling that the Euler characteristic of disjoint sets is equal to the sum of the Euler characteristics of the individual sets and that the Euler characteristic of the product of spaces is equal to the product of the Euler characteristics of the individual spaces.

For example, the straight line, the plane and every Euclidean space have unitary Euler characteristic as well as the projective plane, while the sphere has Euler characteristic equal to 2, the Klein bottle, the Mobius strip and the torus have such value that it is null.

In differential geometry there is the Gauss-Bonnet theorem according to which, for a two-dimensional Riemannian manifold it is compact, the following holds:

$$\int_M KdA + \int_{\partial M} k_g\, ds = 2\pi\chi(M)$$

Where the Gaussian curvature, the geodesic curvature of the boundary and the Euler characteristic of the manifold appear.

Groups and group theory

The first algebraic structure that we present is that of a group, a set provided with a binary operation which enjoys the associative properties, of existence of the neutral element and of the inverse one.
If the commutative property also holds, the group is said to be commutative or abelian.
The cardinality of the group is called order and if it is finite, then the group is said to be finite.
The importance of groups derives from the definition of a theory of groups which is fundamental for the understanding of contemporary physics.
For example, integers with the sum operation are an abelian group, permutations of a set are a group with the function composition operation, a vector space is an abelian group with respect to the sum of vectors.
Particular groups can be defined on matrices such as the orthogonal group, formed by orthogonal square matrices, and the general linear group formed by invertible square matrices; We will explore some of these aspects below.
We define the direct product of two groups as the Cartesian product between them.
There are other types of product between groups, including free and semi-direct products that are based on other rules and which define other product groups.
We say action of a group G on a set A, a function such that:

$$\forall a \in A \Rightarrow e \cdot a = a$$
$$\forall g, h \in G, \forall a \in A \Rightarrow g \cdot (h \cdot a) = (gh) \cdot a$$

The center of a group is the following subset:

$$C := \{c \mid \forall g \in G \Rightarrow c * g = g * c\}$$

The centralizer of an element of a group is the following set:

$$Z(g) := \{h \in G \mid g * h = h * g\}$$

Two elements are inverse if:

$$a * b = b * a = 1$$

Two elements of a group are conjugate if:

$$h^{-1} * a * h = b$$

A class formed only by conjugate elements is called a conjugate class.
A subset H of a group G is a subgroup if it is a group with the operation defined on G; a subgroup of a finite group is finite and one of an abelian group is abelian.
A subset of a given set that is endowed with an algebraic structure is called a set of generators if all the elements of the set can be obtained through combinations of operations defined therein.
For a group, the generator set is the smallest subset that contains that subset.
An ordered group is a group with order structure.
The symmetric group is the group formed by the set of permutations of its elements. The order of the symmetric group is n! and this group is not abelian if n>2.
The aforementioned general linear group, the group of all invertible square matrices over a field K, is denoted by GL(n,K).
The special linear group is the subgroup of such matrices which have unitary determinant and is denoted by SL(n,K).
Such groups are never abelian for n>1, the diagonal matrices are a subgroup of GL(n,R) which is a differentiable manifold.
The orthogonal group of degree n over a field K is the group of orthogonal matrices and is denoted O(n,K).
If K is the set of real numbers, then this group represents the isometries of Euclidean space.
The orthogonal matrices with unitary determinant form a subgroup denoted by SO(n), called the special orthogonal group which is also the group of rotations of the space.
The orthogonal group is a subgroup of the group GL(n,K) and is a differentiable manifold, but it is not connected.

A cyclic group is defined as a group generated by a single element, called the generator of the group.
A cyclic group is always abelian while every finitely generated abelian group is cyclic.

Integers are an example of a cyclic group of infinite order.
The direct product of two cyclic groups has order equal to the product of the orders of the cyclic groups and is cyclic if and only if these orders are coprime.
Every finite group of first order is a cyclic group.
A dicyclic group is a non-abelian group of order 4n that arises from the extension of a cyclic group with another cyclic group of order 2.
We call dihedral group that group of order 2n formed by the isometries of the plane which leave the regular polygons of n sides unchanged.
This group is not abelian.
Given a group G and a subgroup K, this subgroup is normal if:

$$gK = Kg$$

In an abelian group, every subgroup is normal; the kernel of a homomorphism is a normal subgroup of the group; every subgroup of order 2 is normal.
A simple group is a nontrivial group whose only normal subgroups are the trivial subgroup and the group itself.
A cyclic group is simple if and only if its order is a prime number.
We call a Dedekind group that group in which every subspace is normal and a Hamiltonian group a non-abelian group in which every subgroup is normal.
Given a group G and its normal subgroup H, the quotient group of the equivalence classes is defined as:

$$G/H = \{[g] \mid g \in G\}$$

The extension of a group is a group in which there is a normal subgroup that is isomorphic to the starting group.
A group is said to be nilpotent if the chain of normal subgroups thus defined ends in a finite way:

$$\{e\} = Z_0 \subseteq Z_1 \subseteq ... \subseteq Z_n = G$$

Where each individual subgroup is defined as a quotient group having a given center.
A group is said to be solvable if there exists a chain of subgroups where each of them is normal to the next and their quotient group is abelian.
A group is said to be free if there exists a subset such that it is possible to write, in a unique way, each element of the group as a product of a finite number of elements of the subsets and its inverses.

A Lie group is a group having a structure of differentiable manifold such that a morphism is a differentiable homomorphism.
These groups are categories together with their morphisms.
A group presentation is the list of group generators and group relationships. If the set of generators is finite the presentation is said to be finitely generated, if the set of relations is finite it is said to be finitely related.
Each finished group has a finished presentation.
The kernel of a homomorphism between groups is a normal subgroup, while abelian groups have an abelian homomorphism.
Particularly important in physics is the group of quaternions, i.e. the group formed by the eight elements (1, -1, i, -i, j, -j, k, -k). The following relationships hold:

$$i^2 = j^2 = k^2 = -1$$
$$ij = k$$
$$ji = -k$$
$$ik = -j$$
$$ki = k$$
$$jk = i$$
$$kj = -i$$

This group is not abelian but is Hamiltonian and is isomorphic to the group of invertible matrices with complex values.
A non-associative extension of this group is that of the octonions which forms a non-associative 8-dimensional algebra on the field of real numbers; this algebra is the only finite-dimensional non-associative one definable on real numbers.
Actually, the octonions do not form a group but a quasigroup (we will see this definition shortly).
A further extension is that of sedenions, a 16-dimensional algebra on the field of real numbers. As with octonions, the binary operation is neither associative nor commutative.

There are several fundamental theorems in group theory.
Given a topological space X union of two open sets A and B, such that the sets and their intersection are arc-connected, Van Kampen's theorem states that, considered a basis point in the intersection set, the fundamental group of the space topological is given by the following product:

$$\pi(X, x_0) = \pi(A, x_0) * \pi(A \cap B, x_0)\pi(B, x_0)$$

If A and B are simply connected, then so is X.

Sylow's first theorem states that a finite group G admits a subgroup of order equal to a prime number raised to an integer such that their power is a divisor of the order of the group.

If the order of a finite group can be expressed as the product of the power mentioned above and a coprime number at the base of the power, then Sylow's second theorem states that all subgroups of order equal to the power are conjugate.

Sylow's third theorem, having assumptions the same as those of the second, states that the number of subgroups of order equal to the power is divisible by the power base.

The first isomorphism theorem states that the kernel of a homomorphism between groups is a normal subgroup and the quotient group is isomorphic to the codomain of the homomorphism.

The second isomorphism theorem states that given two subgroups of a group, one of which is normal, then their product subset is a subgroup of the group.

Furthermore, the normal subgroup is also normal in the product subset.

The isomorphism induced by the map on the codomain of the quotient group between the product subset and the normal subgroup is called canonical.

The third isomorphism theorem states that given two normal subgroups, one of which is contained in the other, then the following canonical isomorphism holds on quotient groups:

$$(G/N)/(H/N) \cong G/H$$

Lagrange's theorem states that a subgroup of a finite group has order which is a number divisor of the order of the group.

From this it follows that a group that has a prime number of elements is cyclic.

Cauchy's theorem states that given a finite group of order n and a prime number that divides n, then there exists in the group elements of order equal to that prime number.

Semigroups, groupoids, quasigroups and loops

We now introduce other types of algebraic structures.

A semigroup is a set endowed with an associative binary operation; analogous considerations apply to what was done for groups, above all for the character of finiteness and commutativity.

A semigroup with a neutral element is called a monoid: it goes without saying that every group is also a monoid.

Given a commutative semigroup with an equivalence relation on the sum per component, the Grothendieck group of this semigroup is the quotient set and is abelian.

A set having a partial associative function and a total inversion function which is always defined is called a groupoid.

A quasigroup is an algebraic structure similar to that of a group where, however, the associative and existence properties of the neutral element are not required.

The binary operation is defined as follows:

$$a*x=b, \text{ so } x=a\backslash b$$
$$y*a=b, \text{ so } y=b/a$$

and it is called, respectively, left division and right division.

For example, integers with the operation of subtraction form a quasigroup.

The deletion property exists in a quasigroup.

A quasigroup with a neutral element is called a loop, so each element of the loop has a unique left inverse and a unique right inverse; moreover, an associative loop is a group.

Inside the loop it is possible to define the left translations, given by the multiplication "to the left" and the right translations.

All translations of a loop generate a group.

A Moufang loop satisfies the juxtaposition identity which is a weak version of associativity:

$$(a \cdot b) \cdot (c \cdot a) = (a \cdot (b \cdot c)) \cdot a$$

We say left-loop an algebraic structure similar to the loop in which only the binary operation "to the left" is valid:

$$a * x = b \Rightarrow x = a/b$$

Each loop is a left-loop.

Left-loops can be constructed from sections of quotient groups.

Monoids, lattices. magmas

A monoid is an algebraic structure with a single binary operation, called a product.

This structure is closed with respect to the binary operation, has the associative property and the neutral element exists.

As already mentioned, a monoid is a unitary semigroup and a group is a monoid with an inverse element.

We define lattice as a partially ordered set; it is an algebraic structure equipped with two binary operations which are commutative, associative and for which the laws of absorption and idempotence hold.

For example, the natural numbers with the usual order relation are a lattice. The lattices with their homomorphisms form a category.

A lattice is said to be bounded if it has a maximum and a minimum, whereas it is said to be complete if each of its subsets has the lower and the upper bounds.

A lattice is distributive if the distributive laws on the two binary operations hold, while it is said to be modular if the distributivity holds for only one of the binary operations.

Furthermore, a complete lattice which is continuous as an ordered lattice is called continuous and a complete lattice which is algebraic as an ordered lattice is called algebraic.

An ordered subset of a lattice is called a sublattice.

A semilattice has the same properties as a lattice but defined on a single binary operation, called meeting, and not on two.

A magma is an algebraic structure with a single binary operation that satisfies only the closure property.

For what has been said, groups, semigroups, quasigroups, loops, left-loops, monoids, lattices, semilattices are all particular magmas.

A magma can be characterized in various ways, for example on the basis of the properties of commutativity, idempotence, distributivity, mediality, alternativeity and so on.

Rings

Other algebraic structures are more refined than those presented so far.

A ring is defined as a set with two binary operations, called sum and product, such that the set and the sum operation are an abelian group with a neutral element given by zero while the set and the product operation are a semigroup with neutral element given by the unit.

Furthermore, the product is distributive with respect to the sum.

In the rings the binomial expansion holds; furthermore it is not required that the product be commutative, while the sum must be.

A ring in which the product is also commutative is called a commutative ring; every cyclic group is a commutative ring.

A subring is a subgroup of a ring that is closed with respect to the product.

An element of a ring is invertible if there is another element such that the product of the two elements (both the left and right) equals unity.

The direct product of two rings is their Cartesian product.
Examples of rings are spaces of matrices and polynomials.
An element of a ring is said to be irreducible if it is not a unit and cannot be written as a product of two elements that are non-units.

We define an ideal subset of a ring that is closed with respect to the interior sum and product for each element of the ring.
In particular, the subset for which the right product of the two elements is part of the ideal is called right ideal, and the one for which this property holds for the left product is called left ideal.
An ideal that is both right and left is said to be bilateral; if the ring is commutative all ideals are bilateral.
An ideal is called proper if it is a proper subset of the ring, ie if and only if it does not contain the unity of the ring.
The sum and product of ideals are:

$$I + J := \{a + b \mid a \in I, b \in J\}$$
$$IJ := \{a_1 b_1 + \ldots + a_n b_n \mid a_i \in I, b_i \in J, i = 1, 2, \ldots, n; \forall n = 1, 2, \ldots\}$$

The intersection of two ideals is an ideal, the union need not be.
An ideal Q of a ring A is primary if, in the quotient ring A/Q, the set of divisors of zero coincides with that of nilpotent elements.
The expression of that ideal as a finite intersection of primary ideals is called the primary decomposition of an ideal.
The ideal generated by a single element is called the principal ideal.
A ring is called an integrity domain if it is commutative and if the product's vanishing law holds

$$a \cdot b = 0 \Rightarrow a = 0 \vee b = 0$$

The set of integers is an integrity domain, while a non-commutative ring can never be an integrity domain.
A domain of integrity in which every ideal is principal is called a principal ideal domain.
In such domains, an element is prime if and only if it is irreducible.
A unique factorization domain is an integrity domain in which every non-invertible element is a product of prime elements.
In these domains, the notions of prime element and irreducible element coincide.
An integrity domain is said to be Euclidean if it is a commutative ring in which it is possible to perform a Euclidean division operation.
A Euclidean domain is a principal ideal domain.
The characteristic of a ring is the smallest non-zero natural number such that the element given by the sum of unity n times is equal to zero.

If this minimum value does not exist then the characteristic is zero by definition.

The characteristic of a ring is the least common multiple of the characteristics of its elements; furthermore if the ring is an integrity domain, each non-zero element has the same characteristic therefore the characteristic of an integrity domain is equal to zero or a prime number.

A ring with a finite number of elements always has a non-zero characteristic.

A ring extension is a pair of rings, one of which is contained within the other.

A homomorphism between rings is a function between two rings that preserves the two operations of addition and product.

The class of all rings with their homomorphisms is a category.

The kernel of a ring homomorphism is an ideal.

A quasi-ring is an algebraic structure similar to a ring but in which the sum is not required to be commutative and that the distributive law of the product with respect to the sum holds on both sides.

A quasi-ring in which the distributive law holds to the left is called left.

If the quasi-ring contains the element that is neutral with respect to the product, it is called a quasi-ring with unity.

A semi-ring is an algebraic structure in which the binary operations of sum and product are associative, the distributive property of the product with respect to the sum holds, the neutral element for the sum exists and is unique and the null element of the product exists.

From what has been said, each ring is also a semi-ring.

Bodies and fields

A body is a set endowed with two binary operations, called sum and product, for which the set and the sum operation are an abelian group with neutral element, the set and the product operation are a group with unitary element, the product is distributive with respect to the sum.

For example, the set of quaternions is a body.

A field is a set endowed with two binary operations, called sum and product, for which the set and the sum operation are an abelian group with neutral element, the private set of this neutral element and the product operation are a abelian group with unitary element, the product is distributive with respect to the sum.

A field is a commutative ring in which every nonzero element has an inverse and is also a commutative body with respect to the product.

Examples of fields are algebraic numbers, the set of complex numbers, the set of real numbers and that of rational numbers; moreover, every finite integrity domain is a field.

Typically the product of fields is not a field, so RxR is a ring but not a field; the quaternion group is also not a field.

On a field, the only ideals are the null element and the field itself, therefore any non-zero homomorphism between fields is injective.

The fields are integrity domains, Euclidean domains, and unique factorization domains.

A field is said to be finite if it has finite cardinality.

The closed subset with respect to the operations of sum and product, which is itself a field, is called a subfield.

The intersection of all subfields is called the prime or fundamental subfield.

A field such that each element of it is algebraic in the field to be extended is said to be an algebraic extension of a field.

The maximal algebraic extension of a field is its algebraic closure, therefore a field is algebraically closed if it coincides with its algebraic closure.

The normal extension is the one generated by the complete factorization of a set of polynomials; the separable extension is the one generated by the roots of separable polynomials.

A field for which every finite extension is separable is called a perfect field.

All fields having characteristic zero and all finite fields are perfect.

An extension field generated by the complete factorization of a polynomial is called splitting field.

A field with total order is called ordered, while it is called numerical if it is an algebraic extension of the field of rational numbers and is called quadratic if this extension is of degree two.

Finally, a field is called cyclotomic if it is an extension, generated by the root of unity, of the field of rational numbers.

As we have seen, it is possible to associate a field with a field algebra, ie a vector space equipped with a binary operation.

A homomorphism between two algebras over a field is a function such that the properties of additivity, multiplication by a scalar and separation of the product hold.

If this function is bijective then we are witnessing an isomorphism between algebras.

Algebraic topology is that part of mathematics which applies the concepts of advanced algebra and algebraic structures to study topological spaces.

In particular, the low-dimensional topology studies the topological spaces of one, two, three or four dimensions and therefore applied to the straight line, the circumference, the surfaces, the manifolds (in this context the Poincaré conjecture was recently proved).

Of particular importance is algebraic geometry, i.e. the study of the geometry of algebraic varieties.

50

GALOIS THEORY

Symmetric polynomials and Cauchy moduli

A polynomial in n variables with coefficients in a field is said to be symmetric in the variables if it happens that:

$$F(x_1, x_2, ..., x_n) = F(x_{\sigma(1)}, x_{\sigma(2)}, ..., x_{\sigma(n)})$$

Where sigma indicates the permutations of the symmetric group S (Galois group, for the definition see the next chapter).

Of all the symmetric polynomials in the single variables, the elementary symmetric functions have particular importance in which each single permutation is given by the sum of the products of the indices.

In this case, the first permutation is simply the sum of the n variables, the second permutation the sum of the two-by-two products, the third the three-by-three products, and so on.

The sign of each permutation is negative for odd powers and positive for even powers.

It can be shown that the elementary symmetric functions are algebraically independent in the field, i.e.:

$$f(\sigma_1, \sigma_2, ..., \sigma_n) = 0$$

From concepts of elementary algebra it can be seen that if a polynomial assumes the same value u on k distinct points, then this value is the remainder of the division of the polynomial by the product of the single monomials on the distinct points.

Generally this result is known for its consequence given by Ruffini's rule for the decomposition of polynomials.

We define the Cauchy moduli of a polynomial as follows:

$$X_1 = F(X)$$

$$X_2 = \frac{X_1}{x - x_1}$$

...

$$X_n = x - x_n$$

The fundamental theorem of symmetric functions states that given a symmetric polynomial it is a polynomial in the elementary symmetric functions of the single components.

As a corollary it follows that, given a polynomial with coefficients in a field, if its roots are defined in an extension of the field, then the value in the variables of a symmetric polynomial and with coefficients in the field belongs to the field itself.

It further follows that a rational symmetric function is expressed in terms of the elementary symmetric functions of the single variables.

Finally, the expression of a symmetric polynomial in terms of the elementary symmetric functions is unique.

Symmetrical relationships

An algebraic relation over a field is an equality of this type:

$$\varphi(\alpha_1, \alpha_2, ..., \alpha_n) = 0$$

Defined by a polynomial with coefficients in the field:

$$\varphi(x_1, x_2, ..., x_n)$$

Polynomials of this form:

$$X_1(x_1), X_2(x_1, x_2), ..., X_n(x_1, x_2, ..., x_n)$$

They give rise to relationships between the single variables which exist whatever the respective numerical coefficients are (the first for the first term, the first and the second for the second term, etc..).

Such relationships are called symmetric.

The following theorem holds.

Considering a symmetric relation between the roots of a polynomial with coefficients in a field, it holds:

$$\varphi(x_1,..,x_k) = X_1(x_1)q_1(x_1,..,x_k) + ... + X_k(x_1,..,x_k)q_k(x_1,..,x_k)$$

Where q denotes the polynomials in the variables with coefficients in the field.

It can be shown that the Cauchy moduli of a polynomial of degree n form a basis of the ideal of symmetric relations in the variables between the roots of the polynomial.

Galois group

In a field with zero characteristic, we define a separable (but not necessarily irreducible) polynomial of degree n with coefficients defined in the field and roots in a broadening of it.

These roots satisfy some algebraic relations and, under suitable conditions, also some symmetrical relations.

The degree of ambiguity that exists in the determination of the roots starting from the algebraic relations is measured by the permutations that change these relations between the roots into other relations.

These permutations form a group (which is a subgroup of S^n) which is given the name Galois group of the polynomial f(x).

In the Galois group, a rational function of the roots of the polynomial can be expressed as a polynomial of degree lower than the starting polynomial.

In the Galois group, Abel's fundamental theorem holds.

Given two coefficient polynomials g(x) and p(x) in a field K with p(x) irreducible, if g(x) admits a root of p(x) then p(x) divides g(x) and hence g(x) also admits all other roots of p(x).

One of the consequences of this theorem is that it is not possible to algebraically distinguish a number from its conjugates.

Combining these results we have that if a rational function of the roots of a polynomial is zero then the polynomial is identically zero.

Similarly, if the rational function is equal to a constant, the polynomial assumes the value of the constant.

In the Galois group, other results of considerable importance are also valid. For example, the following polynomials:

$$f_k(\alpha_{i_1},...,\alpha_{i_{k-1}},x)$$

They are irreducible in the following field:

$$K(\alpha_{i_1},...,\alpha_{i_{k-1}})$$

Where k can take on all natural integer values from 1 to n.
Moreover:

$$\varphi(\alpha_1,...,\alpha_n)=0 \Rightarrow \varphi(\alpha_{i_1},...,\alpha_{i_n})=0$$

In that case, we have:

$$\alpha_{i_k}(radice)f_k(\alpha_{i_1},...,\alpha_{i_{k-1}},x)$$

So the permutations that change relations into relations form the Galois group.
The order of the Galois group is given by the product of the degrees of the polynomials f.

Fundamental modules and reduction of the Galois group

The polynomials expressed as follows are called fundamental modules of f(x):

$$f_1(x_1),f_2(x_1,x_2),...,f_n(x_1,x_2,...,x_n)$$

This definition, very similar to what was found for symmetrical relations, also involves completely equivalent theorems.
A consequence of all this is that the fundamental modules of the polynomial f(x) are a basis for the ideal of the relations between the roots of f(x).
Stated another way, the Galois group of f(x) consists of the permutations of the roots which preserve the symmetric relations.
Consequently, if a polynomial is equal to a constant then the value of this constant does not change by permuting the roots of the polynomial according to the elements of the Galois group.
In particular, if the polynomial breaks down into linear factors then its Galois group reduces to the identity.

A group of permutations is said to be transitive, if for each i and j there is a permutation of the group which brings i to j.

A group of permutations is called k-transitive if, however given two ordered k-tuples of distinct elements, there exists a permutation of the group which brings the single i onto the single j.

It follows that a Galois group is k-transitive if and only if its fundamental modules coincide in order with the Cauchy modules.

In particular, the Galois group of a polynomial is the entire symmetric group if and only if the fundamental modules and the Cauchy modules of the polynomial coincide.

The set of elements of the Galois group G of a polynomial f(x) which leave the numerical value of a rational function of the roots of f(x) unchanged is a subgroup of G.

Thus, if we broaden the field K by adding a rational function with coefficients in K of the roots of f(x), the Galois group over the broadened field lowers to the above subgroup.

In this case, we speak of a reduction of the Galois group.

An element for which the expanded field coincides with the field of the roots of f(x) is called primitive.

An element is primitive if and only if its images according to the elements of G are all distinct.

In particular, an element is primitive if and only if its subgroup coincides with the identity.

This theorem follows:

given a rational function of the roots and a monic irreducible polynomial J(x) over a field K which admits the rational function as a root, then there exists an integer t such that:

$$J(x)^t = \prod_{\sigma \in G} (x - \gamma^\sigma)$$

So if a root field contains a root of an irreducible polynomial, then it contains them all.

Given a primitive element and defining the following polynomial:

$$\psi(x) = \prod_{\sigma \in G} (x - \gamma^\sigma)$$

The following equation is called the Galois resolvent:

$$\psi(x) = 0$$

An inverse theorem also holds.
Given a subgroup H of G, there exists a primitive element such that H is the reduction of the group G.

Property of the Galois group

A polynomial on K is said to be normal if its roots can be expressed as rational functions on K of any of them.
The irreducible factors of a normal polynomial all have the same degree.
A permutation group in which each element is fixed only by the identity is said to be semiregular.
A semiregular and transitive group is said to be regular.
In a semiregular group, the cycles of a permutation all have the same length and this is equal to the order of the permutation.
The Galois group of f(x) is semiregular if and only if f(x) is a normal polynomial. In this case, f(x)=0 is a Galois resolvent of f(x).
The Galois group of f(x) is regular if and only if f(x) is irreducible and normal. In this case, the order of the group is equal to the degree of f(x).
By adding to a field all the roots of a polynomial f(x), the Galois group of f(x) on the expanded field reduces to a normal subgroup of G.

Extension for abelian groups and primitive groups

If the Galois group G is abelian, then all its subgroups are normal.
Given a normal subgroup in G such that:

$$\vartheta_\sigma(\vartheta_\tau(\gamma)) = \vartheta_\tau(\vartheta_\sigma(\gamma))$$

Then the quotient group given by dividing G by the normal subgroup is abelian.
Given an irreducible polynomial f(x) of degree n is a cyclic group, then the group is generated by a cycle of length n.
The equation f(x)=0 (with f(x) irreducible) is called a cyclic equation.
If f(x) is normal and of prime degree then f(x)=0 is always a cyclic equation.
A transitive abelian group is regular.
It follows that, if the Galois group of an irreducible polynomial is abelian, then the polynomial is normal.

Given a transitive group of a set, a subset such that:

$$\forall \sigma \in G \Rightarrow (\Delta = \Delta^\sigma) \vee (\Delta \cap \Delta^\sigma = 0)$$

Subsets with only one element, the empty set and the starting system are called trivial blocks.
If there are only trivial blocks then the group is called primitive.
Necessary and sufficient condition for an irreducible polynomial f(x) to become reducible in the field expanded with the roots of a polynomial g(x) is that the Galois group of f(x) is not primitive.
A subgroup H formed by block-fixing elements of group G is a normal subgroup of G.
From all this it follows that:
if the Galois group G of an irreducible polynomial f(x) is not primitive, then the polynomial splits into irreducible factors all of equal degree, adding to the field an element fixed by the elements of a subgroup which blocks the systems of imprimitivity of G .
An extension is said to be primitive if every element of it is primitive.
Given a permutation of the Galois group of f(x) on a field K, then the following application:

$$g(\alpha) \to g(\alpha^\sigma)$$

It is well defined.
In this case, the permutation extends to a self-morphism of the field which leaves its elements fixed.

Binomial equations

Given a non-zero element of a field K, we define the following expression as a binomial equation:

$$x^n - a = 0$$

We define Euler function as a function defined for each positive integer n such that: the function in 1 is 1, for the following n the function assumes the value of the number of integers less than n prime with n.
The integers thus defined form a group with respect to modular multiplication and this group is denoted by U(n).

The Galois group G of the binomial equation is a subgroup of the group of linear transformations defined as follows:

$$x \rightarrow kx + t$$
$$(k, n) = 1$$
$$t = 0, 1, ..., (n-1) \bmod n$$

This group has an order given by n times the Euler function calculated in n and the module of G is a divisor of this order.
If k=1 these transformations form a cyclic subgroup of the translations.
This subgroup is normal in the group of linear transformations.
Therefore, the Galois group of the binomial equation is given by the intersection of the Galois group G on the field K with the subgroup of the translations and therefore it is cyclic. Also, it is normal in G and the quotient between G and same is abelian.
The order of the Galois group of the binomial equation is equal to the product of f by the Euler function evaluated in n.
Furthermore, given a prime number p and defined u a p-th primitive root of unity then a binomial equation of the type:

$$x^p - a$$

It is irreducible in both K and K(u).

Solvability by radicals

The equation f(x)=0 with coefficients in a field K is said to be solvable by radicals if there is a sequence of fields

$$K \subset K_1 = K(a_1) \subset ... \subset K_s = K(\alpha)$$

Each successive field is a radical expansion or extension of the field that precedes it.
It follows that a cyclic equation can be solved by radicals.
A consequence of this is that the p-th roots of unity, with p prime number, are expressed by roots with index lower than p.
Furthermore, for each n, the nth roots of unity are expressed by radicals.
A series in which each subgroup is normal in the previous one is called a normal series.

A group which admits a normal series with first order cyclic quotients is said to be solvable.
It can be seen how subgroups and quotients of solvable groups are solvable.
Furthermore, if G is abelian then it is solvable.

The application of Galois theory to equations is easily expressed.
An equation is solvable for roots if and only if its Galois group is solvable.
If we consider a general equation of degree n over K:

$$x^n + a_1 x^{n-1} + \ldots + a_n = 0$$

Galois theory enunciates these two fundamental theorems.

If n is greater than or equal to 5, the symmetric group S^n is not solvable.
Another explanation of this is the following.
Ruffini-Abel theorem: the general equation of degree greater than the fourth is not solvable by radicals.
By introducing seemingly abstract concepts, Galois theory allowed us to prove a basic theorem of algebra.
It can be seen that a first order equation is solvable by radicals if and only if its roots can be expressed as rational functions of any two of them.
More generally, a transitive group G of prime degree is solvable if and only if it contains a cyclic group of prime order as a normal subgroup.
Finally, Kronecker's theorem states that if f(x)=0 is an equation with rational coefficients, irreducible of prime degree and solvable by radicals, then of(x) has only one real root or all roots are real.

Fundamental theorem

The fundamental theorem of Galois theory is as follows.
The correspondence associating the subfield U, between the field K and the field of K on the roots, and the Galois group of f(x) on U. is a one-to-one correspondence between the set of subfields of K on the roots containing K itself is the set of subgroups H of the Galois group G of f(x) on K.
This correspondence is called Galois correspondence.
It can be seen that the Galois correspondence reverses the sense of inclusion.
As a consequence it is that there are a finite number of intermediate fields between K and the field of K on the roots.

Furthermore, in the Galois correspondence, normal subgroups of G correspond to normal broadenings of K.

We define a finite field as a field that has a number of elements that is a power of a prime number p.
The Galois group G of order p of an irreducible polynomial f(x) of degree m over a finite field of order p is cyclic of order m.

The inverse Galois problem

The inverse Galois problem requires establishing whether given a finite group G there exists a field K and a polynomial f(x) such that G is isomorphic to the Galois group of f(x) over K.
If so, G is said to be a Galois group on K.
If G is a finite group and f(x) a polynomial with rational coefficients, then G is the Galois group of f(x) over an expansion of Q, the set of rational numbers.
The same is true if G is a cyclic group or a finite abelian group.

More results

There are other results of Galois theory in algebraics.
The first of them is given by Hilbert's theorem.
Given a polynomial with coefficients in the field of rational functions, then if G is the Galois group of the polynomial in this field, rational numbers can be chosen in infinite ways which transform the coefficients of the initial polynomial into other rational coefficients.
The second is Schur's theorem.
Defined a(m) the number of polynomials of degree na with integer coefficients of absolute value less than or equal to mes(m) the number of those, among these, which have the symmetric group as Galois group on Q, we have:

$$\lim_{m \to \infty} \frac{s(m)}{a(m)} = 1$$

Other results of the Galois theory involve geometric concepts.

The roots of an irreducible polynomial can be constructed with straightedge and compass if and only if the order of the Galois group is a power of 2.

As a corollary, we can say that the regular polygon with n sides can be constructed with straightedge and compass if and only if on is a power of 2 or:

$$n = 2^k p_1 p_2 \cdots p_t$$
$$p = 2^s + 1$$

That is, if the various p are distinct and prime Fermat numbers.

Solving quadratic equations

Given the generic quadratic equation:

$$x^2 + px + q = 0$$

It is shown that the roots must satisfy the following relations:

$$\alpha_1 + \alpha_2 = -p$$
$$\alpha_1 - \alpha_2 = \sqrt{p^2 - 4q}$$

By applying the Galois theory on the splitting field of f(x), we find two linear functions with coefficients related to the second roots of the units -1 and 1.

This leads to the root formula:

$$\alpha_{1,2} = \frac{1}{2}\left[(\alpha_1 + \alpha_2) + \sqrt{(\alpha_1 - \alpha_2)^2}\right]$$

Solving third degree equations

The tertiary equation in reduced form is given by:

$$x^3 + px + q = 0$$

Recall that the reduced form is equivalent, up to substitutions, to the general form. Therefore, by studying the reduced form it is possible to find the solutions of the general one.

Through the procedure of the Lagrange resolvent, whose expression is the following:

$$y^2 + qy - \frac{1}{27}p^3$$

Find the two roots of the resolvent.

From here we can systematize with the condition on the roots of the reduced formula:

$$\alpha_1 + \alpha_2 + \alpha_3 = 0$$

Define the following complex number:

$$w = -\frac{1}{2} + \frac{1}{2}i\sqrt{3}$$

Find the Cardano formulas for the roots of the tertiary equation in reduced form:

$$\alpha_1 = \sqrt[3]{y_1} + \sqrt[3]{y_2}$$
$$\alpha_2 = w\sqrt[3]{y_1} + w^2\sqrt[3]{y_2}$$
$$\alpha_3 = w^2\sqrt[3]{y_1} + w\sqrt[3]{y_2}$$

Solving quadratic equations

The reduced form of the equation is as follows:

$$x^4 + px^2 + qx + r = 0$$

The following roots are found:

$$\alpha_1 = \frac{1}{4}\left(\sqrt{z_1} + \sqrt{z_2} + \sqrt{z_3}\right)$$

$$\alpha_2 = \frac{1}{4}\left(\sqrt{z_1} - \sqrt{z_2} - \sqrt{z_3}\right)$$

$$\alpha_3 = \frac{1}{4}\left(-\sqrt{z_1} + \sqrt{z_2} - \sqrt{z_3}\right)$$

$$\alpha_4 = \frac{1}{4}\left(-\sqrt{z_1} - \sqrt{z_2} + \sqrt{z_3}\right)$$

Where the z's are the solutions of the following quadratic equation:

$$z^3 + 8pz^2 + 16(p^2 - 4r)z - 64q^2 = 0$$

Ruffini-Abel theorem

We define alternating a symmetric function with values of opposite sign.
It is shown that the only functions that can have symmetric powers are the symmetric or alternating functions of algebraically independent variables.
For n greater than four, a function of n algebraically independent variables that has a two-valued power is itself two-valued.
We can define Abel's theorem.
Given n roots of a polynomial with coefficients in a field K, if a root is expressed by radicals of elements not belonging to the field of roots then it is also expressed by radicals of elements belonging to that field.
As a consequence of this, we find, in another way, the Ruffini-Abel theorem.

For n greater than four, the general equation of degree n is not solvable by radicals.

Monodromy

Galois theory can also be useful in the set of complex numbers, as far as complex analysis is concerned.
Consider the Galois group of one-parameter polynomials:

$$f(w,z) = a_0(z)w^n + ... + a_n(z)$$

Called $C(z)$ the field of rational functions with complex coefficients, the Galois group of $f(w,z)$ on $C(z)$ is the group of permutations of the roots that change relations with coefficients in $C(z)$ into other relations .
This group is a subgroup of G, called monodromy group.
Prove that the monodromy group of a polynomial is a normal subgroup of the Galois group of the polynomial itself.
If $f(w,z)$ is irreducible then the roots are distinct and finite except in some critical or singular points.
They can be divided into points where one or more roots become infinite or points where two or more roots coincide.
A function is monodrome if it has no critical points.
It is proved that an algebraic function is monodromous in the whole plane C if and only if it is a rational function.
Recalling what is present in complex analysis about the concepts of closed path, we can state the following Hermite theorem:
the group of permutations induced on the roots of $f(w,z)$ by all the closed paths traversed by z coincides with the monodromy group.

Topological view

Galois theory is a part of abstract algebra and historically arises from the attempt to solve the Abel-Ruffini theorem, according to which there is no solution formula for the roots of a generic polynomial equation of fifth degree or higher using algebraic operations elementary.
Galois theory answers this and other classical questions, such as the impossibility of constructing a square with an area equal to that of a circle.

Given an extension E of a field F, an automorphism which fixes the elements of F is called F-automorphism:

$$\psi : E \rightarrow E \mid \forall x \in F, \psi(x) = x$$

The F-automorphisms of the extension form a group called the Galois group which is denoted by:

$$G = Gal(E / F)$$

The splitting field of a polynomial defined on a field F is defined as an extension of the field in which the polynomial is factorized and the roots generate the extension itself.
Each field has a unique splitting field, up to isomorphisms.
If there exists an algebraically closed field K which contains the field F, then there exists a unique splitting field of the polynomial contained in the field K.

A polynomial is said to be separable if each of its irreducible factors has distinct roots in the splitting field.
All irreducible polynomials that have a zero in a separable extension are separable, so all polynomials having coefficients defined over perfect fields are separable.
Given a separable polynomial with coefficients in a field, the Galois group of the polynomial is the one defined on the extension given by the splitting field of the polynomial in the field.
The Galois group defined on the fields of complex and real numbers Gal(C/R) has two elements given by identity and complex conjugation.
The Galois group defined on the fields of real and rational numbers Gal(R/Q) is trivial having the identity as its only element.
The Galois group defined on fields of complex and rational numbers is infinite.
If F is a finite field with positive characteristic p, then it is an extension of a field and we have that:

$$Gal(F, F_p) = C_n = \langle f \rangle$$

In this case the Galois group is the cyclic group of nth order and f is a Frobenius-defined endomorphism.
An E/F extension is Galois if the fixed field of the Galois group Gal(E/F) coincides with the base field F.
In particular, if E is a field and G is a finite group of automorphisms of E, then the E/F extension is Galois.

Moreover, a finite extension is Galois if and only it is normal and separable or E is the splitting field of a separable polynomial with coefficients in F or if the degree of the extension is equal to the order of the automorphism group of E/ f.

An infinite extension is Galois if and only if it is normal and separable or E is the splitting field of a family of separable polynomials with coefficients in F.

Results of the topological theory

Given an extension of E/F fields with associated Galois group G=Gal(E/F) we define two Galois connections as follows:

1) For each field L between F and E, i(L)=Gal(E/L) is the subgroup of the automorphisms of E that leave the elements of L fixed.

2) For each subgroup H of G, j(H) is the field between F and E consisting of the elements of E which are left fixed by all the automorphisms of H.

The fundamental theorem of Galois theory in the finite case states that the Galois connections thus defined are inverse of each other and therefore there is a bijection between the set of fields between F and E and the subgroups of the Galois group g.

For the infinite case, this theorem states that a bijection is generated between the set of fields between F and E and the set of subgroups of G which are closed with respect to a particular topology, called Krull.

We define a solvable group as a group that has an abelian normal series, i.e. there is a chain of subgroups defined in this way:

$$\{e\} \subseteq H_1 \subseteq \ldots \subseteq H_n = G$$

Where e is the neutral element, each subgroup is normal to the next one and the quotient given by one subgroup and the previous one is abelian.

If G is a finite group the quotients are also cyclic. It is proved that a polynomial is solvable over a field F with characteristic zero if and only if its Galois group over F is solvable.

Through the definition of solvable Galois groups and the fundamental theorem of Galois theory, the Abel-Ruffini theorem can be proved.

It is also possible to solve the inverse Galois problem, that is to determine which groups G are Galois groups of some Galois extension on a fixed field F.

If such an extension exists, G is said to be realizable on F.

There is still no general solution to the inverse problem, only solutions in particular cases.

For finite fields, the Galois group is always cyclic and therefore the inverse problem is easy to solve.

Furthermore, every abelian group is the Galois group of some extension of the field of rational numbers.

With the exception of the Mathieu group, all simple groups can be realized as Galois groups on the field of rational numbers.

Finally, all solvable groups are Galois groups of an extension of the field of rational numbers.

If the field on which to realize the Galois group is not fixed, the inverse Galois problem has a trivial resolution, exploiting the fundamental theorem of Galois theory and Cayley's theorem.

Galois theory is a starting point for other theories, including monodromy studies and Kummer's theory.

The monodromy group of a polynomial is a normal subgroup of the Galois group, furthermore an algebraic function on the whole complex plane is monodromous if and only if it is rational.

We define Kummer extension as an extension of fields L/K such that L is generated on K by a root of the polynomial $x^n - a$ with n>1 and a belonging to K and such that K contains n distinct roots of $x^n - 1$.

These extensions are Galois extensions with a cyclic Galois group.

Kummer's theory studies the inverse case ie, if K contains n distinct n-th roots of unity, then any cyclic extension of K of degree n is obtained by adding an n-th root.

Exercises

Exercise 1

Calculate the Cauchy moduli for a polynomial of degree 3.

The Cauchy modules are:

$$
\begin{aligned}
X_1(x) &= F(x) = x^3 + \sigma_1 x^2 + \sigma_2 x + \sigma_3, \\
X_2(x_1, x) &= (x - x_2)(x - x_3) = x^2 - (x_2 + x_3)x + x_2 x_3 \\
&= x^2 + (x_1 + \sigma_1)x + x_1^2 + \sigma_1 x_1 + \sigma_2 \\
X_3(x_1, x_2, x) &= x - x_3 = x + x_1 + x_2 + \sigma_1,
\end{aligned}
$$

We can rewrite the polynomial as:

$$f(x) = x^3 + e_1 x^2 + e_2 x + e_3$$

Roots:

$$\alpha_1, \alpha_2, \alpha_3$$

Then the modules are:

$$
\begin{aligned}
X_1(x) &= f(x), \\
X_2(\alpha_1, x) &= (x - \alpha_2)(x - \alpha_3) = x^2 - (\alpha_2 + \alpha_3)x + \alpha_2\alpha_3 \\
&= x^2 + (\alpha_1 + e_1)x + \alpha_1^2 + e_1\alpha_1 + e_2 \\
X_3(\alpha_1, \alpha_2, x) &= x - \alpha_3 = x + \alpha_1 + \alpha_2 + e_1.
\end{aligned}
$$

Exercise 2

Calculate the Cauchy moduli for a polynomial of degree 4.

The Cauchy modules are:

$$
\begin{aligned}
X_1 &= F(x) = x^4 + \sigma_1 x^3 + \sigma_2 x^2 + \sigma_3 x + \sigma_4, \\
X_2 &= x^3 + (x_1 + \sigma_1)x^2 + (x_1^2 + \sigma_1 x_1 + \sigma_2)x + x_1^3 + \sigma_1 x_1^2 + \sigma_2 x_1 + \sigma_3, \\
X_3 &= x^2 + (x_1 + x_2 + \sigma_1)x + x_1^2 + x_2^2 + x_1 x_2 + \sigma_1(x_1 + x_2) + \sigma_2, \\
X_4 &= x + x_1 + x_2 + x_3 + \sigma_1,
\end{aligned}
$$

We can rewrite the polynomial as:

$$f(x) = x^4 + e_1 x^3 + e_2 x^2 + e_3 x + e_4$$

Roots:

$$\alpha_1, \alpha_2, \alpha_3, \alpha_4,$$

Then the modules are:

$$
\begin{aligned}
X_1(x) &= f(x), \\
X_2(\alpha_1, x) &= x^3 + (\alpha_1 + e_1)x^2 + (\alpha_1^2 + e_1\alpha_1 + e_2)x + \alpha_1^3 + e_1\alpha_1^2 + e_2\alpha_1 + e_3, \\
X_3(\alpha_1, \alpha_2, x) &= x^2 + (\alpha_1 + \alpha_2 + e_1)x + \alpha_1^2 + \alpha_2^2 + \alpha_1\alpha_2 + e_1(\alpha_1 + \alpha_2) + e_2, \\
X_4(\alpha_1, \alpha_2, \alpha_3, x) &= x + \alpha_1 + \alpha_2 + \alpha_3 + e_1,
\end{aligned}
$$

Exercise 3

Write the symmetric polynomial of:

$$
u = F(x_1, x_2) = x_1^3 + x_2^3.
$$

The polynomial given by:

$$
F(x_1, x) = x^3 + x_1^3
$$

Divided by:

$$
X_2 = x + x_1 + \sigma_1
$$

Provides the rest

$$
F_1(\sigma_1, x_1) = -3\sigma_1 x_1^2 - 3\sigma_1^2 x_1 - \sigma_1^3,
$$

Dividend:

$$
F_1(\sigma_1, x)
$$

For:

$$
X_1 = x^2 + \sigma_1 x + \sigma_2
$$

We have the symmetric polynomial:

$$
F_2(\sigma_1, \sigma_2) = -\sigma_1^3 + 3\sigma_1\sigma_2
$$

Exercise 4

Given the function:

$$f(x) = x^3 + 1$$

Prove that there is a symmetric relation between the roots even though the polynomial is not symmetric.

We immediately notice that:

$$\varphi(x_1, x_2) = x_1^3 - x_2^3,$$

It's not symmetrical.
For the three roots of the polynomial we have:

$$\alpha^3 = -1$$

And then:

$$\alpha_i^3 - \alpha_j^3 = 0.$$

Which is a symmetric relationship between the roots.

Exercise 5

Consider the following polynomial over the rational field Q.

$$f(x) = x^4 - 2$$

Write the irreducible factorization.

The roots are:

$$\alpha_1 = \sqrt[4]{2}, \ \alpha_2 = -\alpha_1, \ \alpha_3 = i\alpha_1, \ \alpha_4 = -i\alpha_1.$$

The factorization in Q is therefore:

$$f(x) = (x - \alpha_1)(x + \alpha_1)(x^2 + \alpha_1^2).$$

The relationships between roots are:

$$\alpha_1^4 = 2, \; \alpha_2 + \alpha_1 = 0, \; \alpha_3^2 - \alpha_1\alpha_2 = 0, \; \alpha_4 + \alpha_3 = 0$$

We divide the polynomial:

$$x_1 x_2 + x_3 x_4.$$

For the last fundamental module:

$$f_4(x_1, x_2, x_3, x_4) = x_4 + x_3.$$

We have:

$$x_3 x_4 + x_1 x_2 = (x_4 + x_3)x_3 - x_3^2 + x_1 x_2.$$

We divide the remainder:

$$-x_3^2 + x_1 x_2$$

For:

$$f_3 = x_3^2 - x_1 x_2:$$

You get:

$$-x_3^2 + x_1 x_2 = (x_3^2 - x_1 x_2) \cdot (-1) + 0,$$

Substituting into the roots, we get the irreducible factorization:

$$\alpha_2\alpha_4 - \alpha_1\alpha_3 = (\alpha_4 + \alpha_3)\alpha_2 + (\alpha_2 + \alpha_1)(-\alpha_3).$$

Exercise 6

Find the Galois group of the polynomial:

$$f(x) = x^4 - 5x^2 + 6 = (x^2 - 2)(x^2 - 3)$$

The roots are:

$$\alpha_{1,2} = \pm\sqrt{2}, \alpha_{3,4} = \pm\sqrt{3}.$$

The relationships between the roots are:

$$\alpha_1^2 - 2 = 0.$$
$$\alpha_2 + \alpha_1 = 0.$$
$$\alpha_3^2 - 3 = 0.$$
$$\alpha_4 + \alpha_3 = 0.$$

The Galois group is:

$$G = \{I, (1,2)(3,4), (1,2)(3)(4), (1)(2)(3,4)\}.$$

Exercise 7

Given:

$$f(x) = (x^2 - 2)(x^2 - 3)$$

Find the order of the Galois group and the minimal polynomial.

The basic modules are:

$$f_1 = x_1^2 - 2, \ f_2 = x_2 + x_1, \ f_3 = x_3^2 - 3, \ f_4 = x_4 + x_3.$$

The order of the Galois group is:

$$m = 2 \cdot 1 \cdot 2 \cdot 1 = 4.$$

By placing:

$$\gamma = \alpha_1 + \alpha_3 \ (= \sqrt{2} + \sqrt{3}),$$

The minimum polynomial is:

$$J(y) = y^4 - 10y^2 + 1$$

Exercise 8

Determine the characteristics of the Galois group of:

$$f(x) = (x^2 + 1)(x^2 + 4)$$

We note that the polynomial is normal and has the following roots:

$$\alpha_1 = i, \alpha_2 = -i, \alpha_3 = 2i, \alpha_4 = -2i$$

They satisfy the relations:

$$\alpha_1^2 + 1 = 0, \ \alpha_2 + \alpha_1 = 0, \ \alpha_3 - 2\alpha_1 = 0, \ \alpha_4 + 2\alpha_1 = 0.$$

The Galois group is given by:

$$G = \{I, (1,2)(3,4)\}$$

Since the cycles (1,2) and (3,4) appear in the group of permutations. The modulus of the Galois group is greater than 1 as no root belongs to Q. So the Galois group is semiregular.

Exercise 9

Calculate the third roots of unity using the method of the Galois theorem.

The Galois group is cyclic and of order 2 and can be expressed as:

$$G = \{I, (\alpha, \vartheta(\alpha))\}$$
$$\vartheta(\alpha) = \alpha^2 ..$$

Calling 1 and -1 the second roots of unity, we have:

$$\psi_0(\alpha) = (\alpha + 1 \cdot \alpha^2)^2 = \alpha^2 + 2\alpha^3 + \alpha^4 = \alpha^2 + \alpha + 2 = 1,$$

Having used the following identities:

$$\alpha^3 = 1$$
$$x^2 + \alpha + 1 = 0$$

Calculating elsewhere:

$$\psi_1(\alpha) = (\alpha - \alpha^2)^2 = \alpha^2 - 2\alpha^3 + \alpha^4 = \alpha^2 - 2 + \alpha = \alpha^2 + \alpha + 1 - 3 = -3,$$

And then:

$$\alpha = \frac{1}{2}(\sqrt[2]{1} + \sqrt[2]{-3}).$$

However:

$$\alpha + \alpha^2 = -1.$$

And it turns out that:

$$\alpha_1 = \frac{1}{2}(-1 + \sqrt[2]{-3}).$$

$$\alpha_2 = \frac{1}{2}(-1 + (-1)^{-1}\sqrt[2]{-3}).$$

Exercise 10

Calculate the roots of:

$$x^3 - 12x + 16 = 0.$$

We have:

$$y_1 = y_2 = -8.$$

For the radicals we choose the determination -2 and therefore:

$$\alpha_1 = \sqrt[3]{-8} + \sqrt[3]{-8} = -2 + (-2) = -4,$$
$$\alpha_2 = w\sqrt[3]{-8} + w^2\sqrt[3]{-8} = (w + w^2)\sqrt[3]{-8} = -1 \cdot -2 = 2$$
$$\alpha_3 = w^2\sqrt[3]{-8} + w\sqrt[3]{-8} = (w^2 + w)\sqrt[3]{-8} = -1 \cdot -2 = 2.$$

Exercise 11

Calculate the roots of:

$$x^3 + x - 2 = 0$$

It is immediate to verify that a root is 1.
We therefore have that:

$$\alpha = \sqrt[3]{1 + \frac{2}{3}\sqrt{\frac{7}{3}}} + \sqrt[3]{1 - \frac{2}{3}\sqrt{\frac{7}{3}}},$$

And then:

$$u = \frac{1}{2} + \frac{1}{2}\sqrt{\frac{7}{3}}$$
$$v = \frac{1}{2} - \frac{1}{2}\sqrt{\frac{7}{3}}.$$

From which the three roots are obtained:

$$\alpha_1 = u + v = 1, \ \alpha_2 = wu + w^2v = -1 + \frac{1}{2}i\sqrt{7}, \ \alpha_3 = w^2u + wv = -1 - \frac{1}{2}i\sqrt{7}.$$

Exercise 12

Calculate the roots of:

$$x^3 - 15x - 4 = 0$$

It is immediate to verify that a root is 4.
We have that, dividing by x-4 we obtain the other two real roots:

$$-2 \pm \sqrt{3}:$$

Exercise 13

Given the polynomial:

$$f(w, z) = w^2 - z$$

Calculate singularities and critical points.

The polynomial is irreducible.
The discriminant is:

$$D(z) = \det\left(\begin{pmatrix} 1 & 0 & -z \\ 2 & 0 & 0 \\ 0 & 2 & 0 \end{pmatrix} \right) = -4z.$$

It vanishes for z=0 and therefore this point is a singularity.
For the infinitive, we substitute:

$$z = z_1^{-1}$$

We have:

$$g(w, z_1) = z_1 w^2 - 1$$

Whose discriminant is:

$$D_1(z_1) = -1 \cdot \frac{1}{z} \cdot \det\left(\begin{array}{ccc} z_1 & 0 & -1 \\ 2z_1 & 0 & 0 \\ 0 & 2z_1 & 0 \end{array}\right) = -1 \cdot \frac{1}{z}(-4z_1^2) = 4z_1$$

So infinity is a critical point for f.

Exercise 14

Given the polynomial:

$$f(w, z) = zw^2 - zw - 1.$$

Finding singularities and critical points.

The discriminant is:

$$D(z) = z(z+4)$$

z=0 and z=-4 are singular points.
For the infinitive, we substitute:

$$z = z_1^{-1}$$

We have:

$$g(w, z_1) = w^2 - w - z_1,$$

Whose discriminant is:

$$D'(z_1) = 4z_1 + 1$$

So infinity is not a critical point for f.

Exercise 15

Given:

$$f(w, z) = w^4 - 2w^2 + 1 - z.$$

Classify singularities.

Place:

$$w^2 = t.$$

The four roots are:

$$w_1 = \sqrt{1 + \sqrt{z}}, \; w_2 = \sqrt{1 - \sqrt{z}}, \; w_3 = -\sqrt{1 + \sqrt{z}}, \; w_4 = -\sqrt{1 - \sqrt{z}}.$$

The discriminant is:

$$D(z) = -256(z - 1)z^2,$$

The singularities are 0 and 1.
For z=0 we have:

$$f(w, 0) = w^4 - 2w^2 + 1 = (w^2 - 1)^2,$$

The first two roots coincide and are worth 1, the same goes for the last two roots which are worth -1.
Therefore 0 is a branch point.
For z=1 we have that, after one revolution around this point, the even roots exchange each other since:

$$1 - \sqrt{z} = \rho e^{i\theta'}$$

$$w_2 = \sqrt{1 - \sqrt{z}} = \rho^{\frac{1}{2}} e^{i\frac{\theta}{2}} \longrightarrow \rho^{\frac{1}{2}} e^{i(\frac{\theta}{2} + \pi)} = -\sqrt{1 - \sqrt{z}} = w_4 .$$

1412

While the odd roots return on themselves.
So point 1 is not branching.
For infinity, if we substitute:

$$z = z_1^{-1}$$

We find a polynomial with discriminant:

$$256(z_1 - 1)z_1^3$$

And therefore infinity is a critical point.

51

COMBINATORY GEOMETRY

Introduction

Combinatorial geometry studies finite or countable sets of objects that satisfy the properties of membership and order.
In the first instance it can be said that this discipline of mathematics generalizes the concepts of combinatorics in relation to particular geometric structures, such as graphs, trees and drawings. Furthermore, combinatorial geometry is part of discrete mathematics.

Graphs

A graph G is an ordered pair of sets V and E, where V is the set of nodes and E the set of edges such that the elements of E are pairs of elements of V.
Two nodes joined by an arc are called endpoints of the arc and the arc is identified by the pair of numbers of its endpoints.
An arc having two coincident extremes is called a loop, while multiple arcs joining the same extremes generate a multi-arc.
A graph without loops and multi-edges is called simple, otherwise it is called multi-graph.
The graph obtained by eliminating all loops and replacing each multi-edge with a single edge having the same endpoints is called a skeleton of a graph.
The number of edges existing on a node is called the degree of the node.
The minimum and maximum degree of a graph are, respectively, the degree of the node with the minimum number of subsistent edges and the degree of the node with the maximum number of subsistent edges.
A graph is said to be regular when the maximum and minimum degree coincide and, in this case, the graph is said to be regular of order equal to the degree.

A graph is said to be planar if, in the plane, the edges intersect only at the nodes.

A planar graph is said to be maximal if, with the addition of any new node, it is no longer planar.

Every planar graph without loops is tetrapartite, i.e. it respects the four color theorem.

A graph without edges is called a null graph, in particular the graph which contains neither edges nor nodes is null.

If a path exists between two nodes, they are said to be connected.

A graph is connected if all of its nodes are connected.

The adjacency of a node is the set of nodes connected to the reference node.

In a connected graph, the eccentricity of a node is the maximum distance from one node to another.

The connection relation between the nodes is an equivalence relation and, in the single equivalence classes, subgraphs can be defined.

An isolated node is a node that is not connected to any other node and that node has degree zero.

A connected planar graph drawn without boundary intersections has Euler characteristic equal to two.

A graph defined with a set of nodes W, a subset of V, is called an induced subgraph with respect to the starting graph.

A directed graph is characterized by directed arcs, that is by arcs that have a direction: a node reached at the entrance by an directed arc is called head, one reached at the exit is called tail.

In a directed graph there is an order relation between the nodes.

In an undirected graph there are no directed edges and the relationship between the edges is symmetric.

A simple graph has no directed edges.

An undirected graph is complete if any two of its nodes are adjacent.

Calling N the number of nodes, the number of edges of a complete graph is equal to:

$$\frac{N(N-1)}{2}$$

The maximum cardinality of a complete subgraph of a graph is called the density of the graph.

It is called a clique of an undirected graph, a complete subgraph such that all nodes of the clique are pairwise adjacent and no other complete subgraph contains the clique.

An ordering of the nodes of an undirected graph is said to be perfect if the intersection between the adjacency and the ordered nodes is a complete subgraph.

In a directed graph, a parent of a node is a node such that the directed pair between it and the node belongs to the edge set.
Similarly, a child of a node is a node such that the directed pair between the node and the child belongs to the arc set.
A node that has no parents is called a root.

A path of given length is an ordered sequence of nodes and a sequence of edges connecting them.
The first and last nodes are called endpoints of the path.
A path with pairwise distinct sides is called a path.
A closed path is called a cycle; a loop is said to be simple if it does not pass through the same node twice.
In an undirected graph, the tour of the graph is a cycle that passes through each node only once.

A chain is a sequence of nodes and a sequence of edges connecting them where the ordering of the sequence does not matter.
A chain is called cyclic if the initial node coincides with the final one; moreover, for an undirected graph, the concept of chain and that of path are equivalent.
Also in an undirected graph, a simple path or cycle has a chord if there is an arc between two non-consecutive nodes of the cycle.
An undirected graph is said to be triangulated if every cycle of length greater than or equal to four has a chord.

A forest is a graph in which each node has, at most, one parent.
The nodes without parents are called roots, those without children are the leaves, while the sequences of arcs are called branches.
It goes without saying that a forest has no cycles.
A graph is said to be bipartite if the set of nodes can be divided into two subsets such that each node of one subset is connected only to a node of the other subset.
A bipartite graph therefore has the set of nodes given by the union of two subsets.
All undirected and noncyclic graphs are bipartite as are cyclic graphs but with an even number of nodes.
The union of bipartite graphs gives rise to other bipartite graphs.
A bipartite graph is convex if there is an ordering in one of the two subsets that respects the adjacency property.
If the adjacency property is respected by the orderings in both subsets, the graph is said to be biconvex.
A bipartite graph is said to be complete if there are all edges connecting the elements of one subset with those of the other.
A dual graph of a planar graph is a graph that has a node for each region of the planar graph and each edge for each edge of the planar graph.

The dual of a planar graph is planar.

The duality property is invertible if the starting graph is also connected.

A graph in which the relationship between the number of nodes and the number of arcs is exponential with a negative exponent is called a scale-free network.

A scale-free network is represented, for example, by the Internet and by the models on which social networks are based.

A random graph is a graph generated by a random variable having a given probability distribution. Random graphs give rise to random networks.

Trees

A tree is an undirected graph in which any two nodes are connected by one and only one path.

The tree is therefore a particular planar, bipartite, connected and acyclic graph; moreover it is also a connected forest: consequently a forest is a disjoint union of trees.

The tree is a connected graph that has the minimum number of nodes to maintain the connection property.

The level of a root is zero, that of a generic node is one plus the level of the parent; the height of a tree is the maximum among the levels of all its nodes.

A binary tree is a tree in which each parent has at most two children.

For a binary tree the height is given by

$$\log_2 k$$

where k is the number of leaves.

The path length of a binary tree is the sum of the node levels.

Every tree with a number greater than or equal to two nodes has at least two leaves.

Every tree with n nodes has n-1 edges. Furthermore, there is only one path between any pair of nodes.

A rooted tree is said to be rooted, a tree is ordered if it is rooted and the children of each root are fully ordered.

A spanning tree of a connected and undirected graph is a tree containing all the vertices of the graph but only a subset of the edges, in particular only those necessary for the connection between all vertices with a single path.

There are various computational algorithms for combinatorial geometry, in particular Kruskal's algorithm calculates spanning trees of minimum total weight, Dijistra's algorithm searches for shortest paths in a cyclic graph, Boruvka's algorithm defines the minimum spanning tree of a graph in which the weight of each pair of arcs is distinct.
Combinatorial geometry also deals with design theory.
A drawing is an ordered pair of sets V and B, where V is a set of positive cardinality of elements called points and B is a set of parts (called blocks) of V, each with a smaller cardinality than that of V. For each drawing an incidence matrix can be associated; from the study of these matrices the main properties of the drawings are obtained.

52

NUMBER THEORY

Definitions

Number theory deals mainly with pure mathematics problems related to integers.
At a basic level, number theory problems concern the concepts of divisibility, Euclid's algorithm for the greatest common divisor and least common multiple.
At an advanced level, number theory searches for the relationships between the various types of prime numbers, sequences of integers and some particular functions, such as those of Euler, establishing numerous conjectures.

A natural number is said to be perfect when it is equal to the sum of its proper divisors, defective when it is greater than the sum of its proper divisors, and abundant when it is less than this sum.
All prime numbers and their powers are defective numbers as are all proper divisors of defective numbers and perfect numbers.
All integer multiples of abundant numbers and perfect numbers are abundant numbers.
A natural number is said to be slightly defective if the sum of its proper divisors is equal to the number minus one and is said to be slightly abundant if this sum is equal to the number plus one.
All powers of two are slightly defective numbers.
A natural number is said to be semi-perfect if it is equal to the sum of some of its divisors.
A semi-perfect number cannot be defective, but it can be abundant.

Modular arithmetic

One can construct an arithmetic of the integers with a congruence relation called module n: this arithmetic takes the name of modular.

Given three integers a, b, n with n different from zero, then a and b are congruent modulo n if their difference is a multiple of n and it is written like this:

$$a \equiv b \pmod{n}$$

This congruence is an equivalence relation, holding the reflexive, symmetric and transitive properties.
Furthermore, congruence is invariant under addition, multiplication and exponentiation and therefore the commutative, associative and distributive properties are also valid.
However, the product of two non-zero elements can give a null result provided that n is not a prime number.
This congruence relation forms a finite cyclic group, therefore abelian; with the operations of sum and product, it forms a ring.

Remarkable theorems

Fermat's little theorem states that given a prime number p, for every integer a the following relation holds:

$$a^{p} \equiv a \pmod{p}$$

This means that, if p is prime and a is a coprime number ap, then:

$$a^{p-1} \equiv 1 \pmod{p}$$

We define the φ Euler function, also called the totient function, as the number of integers between 1 and n that are coprime to n.
The totient function of the product is equal to the product of the totient functions, furthermore if p is a prime number and k>0 we have that:

$$\varphi(p^{k}) = (p-1)p^{k-1} \Leftrightarrow \varphi(p) = p - 1$$

For n greater than or equal to three, the Euler function is even. A number for which the following equation has no solution is said to be nontient:

$$\varphi(x) = n$$

All prime numbers except one are non-living. A number for which the following relation holds is called cocotient:

$$x - \varphi(x) = n$$

If there are no solutions, the number is said to be non-cotient.

Euler's theorem states that, if n is a positive integer and a is coprime with respect to n, then the following relation holds:

$$a^{\varphi(n)} \equiv 1 \pmod{n}$$

This theorem is a generalization of Fermat's little theorem.
A Fermat number is an integer that can be expressed in this form:

$$n \in N \Rightarrow F_n = 2^{2^n} + 1$$

A prime number such that the previous relation also holds is called a Fermat prime.
In a binary number system, all Fermat numbers are palindromes and all Fermat primes are palindrome primes.
Since there are infinitely many Fermat numbers and every prime number divides at most one Fermat number, it remains proven that the prime numbers are infinite.
Furthermore, no Fermat number can be expressed as the sum of two prime numbers, and the sum of the reciprocals of all Fermat numbers is irrational.
Fermat's primality test is derived from Fermat's little theorem.
If there exists a number a such that Fermat's little theorem does not hold for a given n, then n is not prime.
We can define a pseudoprime as a number that behaves like a prime number, even if it is not prime. In particular, a number that respects Fermat's little theorem and Fermat's primality test, even if it is not a prime number, is called Fermat's pseudoprime.
A pseudoprime Fermat number with respect to every a coprime is called a Carmichael number.
A positive integer is a Carmichael number if and only if it is square-free and, for any prime divisor p of n, (p-1) divides (n-1).
From this it follows that all Carmichael numbers are odd, furthermore all Carmichael numbers satisfy Fermat's test of primality.
We can define the Carmichael function as:

$$\lambda(n) = mcm\left(\left\{\varphi(p_i^i)\right\}\right)$$

Where the different p take into account the factorization into prime numbers.

Carmichael's theorem states that, given integer coprime with n, then the Carmichael function of n is the smallest positive integer m such that the following relation holds:

$$a^m \equiv 1 \ (\mathrm{mod}\, n)$$

This theorem generalizes Euler's one.

Types of numbers

A number is called Euler pseudoprime based on if it is a composite odd number and is:

$$a^{\frac{n-1}{2}} \equiv \pm 1 \ (\mathrm{mod}\, n)$$

Every Euler pseudoprime is also a Fermat pseudoprime.

Euler pseudoprime numbers which are coprime in any base are called absolute Euler pseudoprimes and are a subset of the Carmichael numbers.

Given a prime number p and an integer a, the Legendre symbol is defined as follows:

$$\left(\frac{a}{p}\right) = \begin{cases} 0 \Leftrightarrow \dfrac{a}{p} = n \in N \\ 1 \Leftrightarrow \exists k \in N : k^2 \equiv a (\mathrm{mod}\, p) \\ -1 \Leftrightarrow \exists k \in N : k^2 \neq a (\mathrm{mod}\, p) \end{cases}$$

If p is any integer, the Legendre symbol is generalized from the Jacobi symbol.

Legendre's symbol is a fully multiplicative function, furthermore the quadratic reciprocity law (or Gauss's golden theorem) holds:

$$\left(\frac{q}{p}\right) = \left(\frac{p}{q}\right)(-1)^{\left(\frac{p-1}{2}\right)\left(\frac{q-1}{2}\right)}$$

A number is called Euler-Jacobi pseudoprime if this relation holds:

$$a^{\frac{n-1}{2}} \equiv \left(\frac{a}{n}\right) \pmod{n}$$

All Euler-Jacobi pseudoprimes are Euler pseudoprimes.
A number is said to be Mersenne if it can be expressed as follows:

$$M_n = 2^n - 1$$

Where n is a prime positive integer.
If the Mersenne number is prime, we have a Mersenne prime.
All perfect numbers can be expressed in Mersenne numbers as follows:

$$\frac{M_n(M_n+1)}{2} = 2^{n-1}(2^n - 1)$$

Related to the Mersenne numbers is the Lucas-Lehmer primality test.
We define a recursive sequence like this:

$$L_1 = 4$$
$$L_{n-1} = L_n^2 - 2$$

The Lucas-Lehmer primality test states that, given a prime integer, the corresponding Mersenne number is prime if and only if:

$$L_{n-1} \equiv 0 \pmod{M_n}$$

Wilson's theorem states that a natural number greater than one is a prime number if and only if the following relation holds:

$$(n-1)! \equiv -1 \pmod{n}$$

Wilson's primality test derives from this theorem, which however is not applicable in computational problems given the intervention of the factorial operation, which is particularly onerous due to the complexity of the algorithm.

Functions and other theorems

A result of modular arithmetic is the so-called Chinese remainder theorem. Given k pairwise coprime integers, then however we choose a basis of other k integers, there exists an integer solution of the following system of congruences:

$$\forall i = 1,...,k \mid x \equiv a_i \ (\mathrm{mod}\, n_i)$$

All the solutions of this system are congruent in modulus to the product of the n k-ths. We can generalize this theorem to algebraic structures such as groups and rings.

The Mobius function is equal to -1 if the positive integer can be decomposed into an odd number of distinct prime factors, it is equal to 0 if there are one or more repeating prime factors and it is +1 if the number can be decomposed into an even number of distinct prime factors.
This function is multiplicative if the integers are coprime and the sum of all the values of the function on all the divisors of an integer is equal to zero, except for n=1 in which the sum is equal to one.

The Mertens function associates to each positive integer n, an integer obtained as the sum of the values of the Mobius function between 1 and n. It can be written like this:

$$M(n) = \sum_{k=1}^{n} \mu(k)$$

Where in the summation there is the Mobius function. For the Mertens function the following relation holds:

$$\left| M(n) \right| \leq n$$

For every real number, defined as a function that is equal to the number of primes less than or equal to the number, the prime number theorem states that this function tends asymptotically to the ratio between the number and its natural logarithm:

$$\pi(x) \propto \frac{x}{\ln x}$$

A famous number theory theorem recently proved (1994) is Fermat's Last Theorem. It states that there are no positive integer solutions, for n>2, to the following equation:

$$a^n + b^n = c^n$$

The theory of numbers has a particular sector, called analytic theory of numbers, in which the methods of mathematical analysis are used to apply them to the theory of numbers.
An example has just been given via the prime number theorem, while another is given by the Riemann Hypothesis.
This hypothesis constitutes Hilbert's problem 8 (being part of the famous 24 Hilbert problems posed at the beginning of the twentieth century).
The hypothesis is a conjecture on the distribution of non-trivial zeros of the Riemann zeta function defined on a complex number with real part greater than one and analytically extendable by means of meromorphic functions.
The Riemann Hypothesis states that the real part of any nontrivial root is ½.
It has not yet been demonstrated, however it is considered a conjecture because it is believed to be true.
There is a link between this hypothesis and the prime numbers, given that for every real number greater than one the Euler product formula calculated on the prime numbers is valid therefore the distribution of the zeros of the zeta function is linked to the distribution of the prime numbers in the set of numbers natural.

Another result is given by Matiyasevich's theorem which answers Hilbert's tenth problem in the negative: it is not possible to construct a general algorithm to establish whether a system of Diophantine equations has integer solutions.
This theorem states that every recursively countable set is Diophantine.

Conjecture

An unsolved conjecture is that of Collatz: given a positive integer, if it is one the algorithm terminates, if it is even it is divided by two, otherwise it is multiplied by three and one is added.

The conjecture states that this algorithm always fails, regardless of the starting value.

One can formulate this conjecture in terms of algebraic structures and combinatorial geometry.

The Wagstaff number is defined as a prime number of the form:

$$p = \frac{2^q + 1}{3}$$

With q prime number.

Mersenne's new conjecture states that for any odd natural number, if at least two of the following statements are true, then the third is also true.

The three statements are: p is a Mersenne prime, p is a Wagstaff prime, p is expressed in these two alternative ways, for some natural k:

$$p = 2^k \pm 1$$
$$p = 4^k \pm 3$$

This conjecture is also not yet proven.

However, the classical Mersenne conjecture is not true.

We call twin primes two prime numbers that differ from each other by two. They are called cousins, primes that differ by four and sexy primes that differ by six.

A Sophie Germain prime is a prime p such that 2p+1 is also prime (the latter number is called a sure prime).

Sophie Germain's primes are related to Mersenne's primes and Fermat's last theorem.

The twin prime conjecture states that there are infinitely many prime numbers p such that p+2 is prime.

Polignac's conjecture generalizes this result by stating that, for any natural number k, there are infinitely many pairs of primes that differ by 2k.

These conjectures are unproven.

The Hardy-Littlewood conjecture concerns the distribution of twin prime numbers and is an analogue of the prime number theorem.

Another famous unproven conjecture is Goldbach's conjecture in both its strong and weak forms.

The first states that every even number greater than two can be written as the sum of two prime numbers, while the second formulates the same problem by saying that every odd number greater than seven can be expressed as the sum of three odd prime numbers.

The strong conjecture implies the weak one, moreover there are modern results that indicate that the generalized Riemann hypothesis implies the Goldbach conjecture, while lately there have been significant steps towards the possible proof of the conjecture in weak form.

53

ADVANCED MATHEMATICAL LOGIC

Order theory

The theory of orders studies some binary relationships that induce an ordering of the elements.

A binary relation is called order if the reflexive, antisymmetric and transitive properties hold and the set in which this relation holds is called ordered.

A binary relation that satisfies only the reflexive and transitive properties is called a preorder.

If instead of the reflexive property, there is the anti-reflexive one, then we speak of strict order or preorder.

If the order or preorder relation is satisfied for all elements of the set, then we speak of total order or preorder.

Through an equivalence relation and the use of the quotient set, it is always possible to construct an order starting from a preorder.

Within an order we call minimum (or maximum) the smallest (or largest) value assumed in the reference set.

If these values are unique, we speak of a minimum and a maximum.

The maximum (minimum) value in that subset is called the major (or minor) of a subset.

The upper bound is the minimum of the set of majorants, the lower bound is the maximum of the set of minorants.

A subset with a major and a minor is called bounded.

It can be seen that the minimum and the maximum may not exist, but there could be multiple minimal or maximal elements, furthermore the same element can be minimal and maximal.

In order theory, the logical principle of duality holds, i.e. if a given proposition is true for every partially ordered set, then its dual proposition is still true for every partially ordered set.

The proposition obtained by exchanging every inequality and inverting every term with its symmetric is called dual.

A monotonic function is an order-preserving function, so if x<y then also f(x)<f(y) and if the converse is also true, the function is an order embedding.

A surjective order embedding is an order isomorphism.

A well-order is a total order in which every non-empty subset has minimal element. It is partial if the minimal elements are finite in number.

A lattice is an ordered set in which every finite subset has infimum and infimum and is said to be complete if every subset of it (therefore also the non-finite ones) has infimum and infimum.

On a lattice, by defining two binary operations of upper and lower, an algebraic structure is generated.

The well-ordering theorem states that every set can be well-ordered.

Zorn's lemma states that, given a non-empty set in which a partial order relation is defined such that every chain has an upper bound, then such a set contains at least one maximal element.

Zorn's lemma implies the well-ordering theorem.

A theory is said to be of the first order if it is possible to express statements and logically deduce theses in a formal way within the set of definition and not in its subsets.

On the other hand, those in which one can range even within the subsets are called second-order theories.

To formulate a first-order theory, a finite set of symbols, called the alphabet, is needed, a first-order language given by a set of well-formed formulas, a set of logical axioms for logical connectives and quantifiers, a set of proper axioms not deducible from logical ones and a set of inference rules.

A formula that derives from a formal proof is said to be provable.

A first-order theory is syntactically complete if every formula is demonstrable or if its negation is, while it is said to be syntactically consistent if there is no formula for which the formula and its negation are demonstrable at the same time.

A first-order language is characterized by an alphabet of symbols, a set of terms, and formulas.

The alphabet includes symbols for variables, constants, relations, functions, quantifiers, logical connectives, and punctuation.

The terms are the individual constants and the variables.

Within a formula it is possible to identify sub-formulas: a variable is called free if it does not appear in any sub-formula, otherwise it is called constrained.

A well-formed formula that does not contain free variables is called a closed formula, otherwise it is called an open one. Finally, a first-order language has its own semantics, i.e. a correct formation of sentences such as to be able to create a model for the language.

We define first-order arithmetic language as the first-order language through which it is possible to derive formal theories of arithmetic.
The standard model of this language is that of the set of natural numbers with the successor function, defining the symbols of the operations of addition and multiplication and the relation of equality.
A set or property is expressible if there is an open formula that makes it explicit. For example, all recursive sets are expressible.
Given a subset of the set of natural numbers, it is said to be representable if there exists a well-formed formula with a free variable expressing the subset and if, for each natural number belonging to the subset, the formula is provable (or equivalently if for every natural number not belonging to the subset the negation of the formula is demonstrable).
A function is said to be weakly representable if there is a well-formed formula with two free variables that express the function and if, for each pair of natural numbers related to each other through the function, the formula is demonstrable.
A function is highly representable if the additional condition given by the fact that the function expressed by the formula also behaves as a function on the natural number also holds.

Robinson and Peano arithmetic

A first-order theory is Robinson arithmetic denoted by Q whose language is that of first-order arithmetic.
The axioms of Q are the logical ones, those of equality are the following proper axioms:

1) 0 is not a successor of any number.
2) Different numbers have different successors, i.e. the successor function is injective.
3) Every number other than 0 is a successor of some other number.
4) Addition can be defined recursively.
5) Multiplication can be defined recursively.

Q is an incomplete theory, in fact it is not possible to deduce the commutative property of addition.
Robinson's arithmetic is closely related to that of Peano, denoted by PA.
The axioms of PA are the logical ones, those of equality while the proper axioms are those of Robinson with the addition of the principle of induction.

With this addition, the commutative property of addition can be deduced.
To tell the truth, both arithmetic are based on Peano's axioms which define, at an axiomatic level, the set of natural numbers.

Peano's axioms
1) There is a natural number 0.
2) Every natural number has a natural successor number.
3) Different numbers have different successors.
4) 0 is not a successor of any natural number.
5) Every subset of natural numbers which contains zero and the successor of each of its elements coincides with the entire set of natural numbers.

These axioms are all independent of each other; the last axiom is that of induction.
The triad given by the set of natural numbers, zero and the successor function is characterized by the Peano axioms, up to isomorphisms.
Any triad formed by a set, a zero and a function and which satisfies the Peano axioms is called a Peano system.
The categoricity theorem states that all Peano systems are isomorphic to the triad given by the set of natural numbers, zero and the successor function.
Peano's axioms are one of the most famous axiomatic systems.
An axiomatic system is coherent if it is not possible to derive two contradictory theorems from it, it is independent if each of its axioms is independent and it is complete if it is possible to demonstrate from the axioms the truth or falsehood of each proposition.
We shall shortly see the remarkable results of contemporary mathematical logic regarding these properties of axiomatic systems.

Axiomatic systems

An axiomatic system is said to be coherent or consistent if it is impossible to prove a contradiction.
Syntactic consistency is such if both a well-formed formula and its negation cannot be proved at the same time. Semantic coherence is such if the theory admits at least one model.
For a first order theory the two concepts of coherence just exposed are equivalent.
An axiomatic system is correct if every conclusion is a logical consequence of the axioms.
A first-order axiomatic system is syntactically complete if it is possible to prove or disprove any statement in the language of the system, which means that there is no undecidable statement.

A first-order axiomatic system is semantically complete if any formula can be proved to be true in the model.

Syntactic completeness is a stronger property than semantic one.

A first-order theory is said to be satisfiable if there is a model that makes all the formulas of the theory true.

The following notable theorems hold:

1) Weak completeness theorem: a theory is satisfiable if and only if the union of the trees of the sequence built starting from the theory is an open tree.

2) Strong completeness theorem: a theory is unsatisfiable if and only if there exists a natural number such that the tree of the sequence is closed.

3) Syntactic compactness theorem: a theory has a closed tree if and only if there is a closed finite subset.

4) Semantic compactness theorem: if every subset of a set of formulas is satisfiable then so is the set. This theorem simplifies for first-order languages: if every finite subset of in a set of formulas has a model then the set has one too.

5) Semidecidability theorem: the union of the trees of the sequence built starting from the theory is a closed tree if and only if there exists a natural number such that the tree of the sequence is closed.

6) Lowenheim-Skolem theorem: if a set of statements has an infinite model then it has a model of any cardinality greater than or equal to the cardinality of the language.

Axiomatic set theory

In addition to the classical definition of sets, called naive set theory, it is also possible to define an axiomatic theory of sets.

To tell the truth, there are several axiomatic theories of sets that we are now going to explain.

The naïve set theory was shelved after the evidence of numerous paradoxes.

A first axiomatization was given by Zermelo, but was immediately expanded by Fraenkel to give life to the theory of Zermelo-Fraenkel sets.

This theory is based on a first-order language and nine axioms:

1) Extensionality axiom: two sets are equal if and only if they have the same elements.

2) Axiom of the empty set: there exists a set without elements called empty set.

3) Couple axiom: given two sets, then the set that contains only these two sets is a set.

4) Union axiom: every set has a union.

5) Axiom of infinity: there exists a set x such that {} is in x and whenever y is in x, so is the union between y and {y}.

6) Separation axiom: given a set and a generic proposition, there exists a subset that contains the elements for which the proposition holds.

7) Replacement axiom: given a set and an application, there exists a set that contains the images of the elements of the original set according to that application.

8) Power set axiom: for each set x there is a set y such that the elements of y are the subsets of x.

9) Axiom of regularity: every non-empty set contains a given element such that the set and the element are disjoint.

However, some results of logic are not demonstrable only with these nine axioms.

A further axiom must be introduced, called the axiom of choice, which gives rise to the axiomatic theory of sets ZFC (where C stands for choice).

The axiom of choice states that, given a non-empty family of non-empty sets, there exists a function which makes one element correspond to each set of the family.

The axiom of choice is necessary for the proof that every vector space admits a basis and for the proof of various theorems (that of Hahn-Banach and that of semantic compactness, for example).

It can be seen that the axiom of choice is equivalent to Zorn's lemma, to the well-ordering theorem and to the following Hartogs theorem: given two sets, one always has that the cardinality of one is greater than or equal to or less than or equal to the cardinality of the other so all sets have comparable cardinality even if they are unbounded.

The axiom of countable choice is a weak version of the axiom of choice and states that every countable collection of non-empty sets has a choice function.

This axiom is not provable in Zermelo-Fraenkel set theory without introducing the axiom of choice.

From the ZFC axioms all other mathematical concepts are constructed, such as those of number, order, relation and function.

There are some propositions that are independent of ZFC, among these we mention:

1) Cantor's continuum hypothesis: there is no set whose cardinality is strictly between that of integers and that of real numbers.

2) Suslin's hypothesis: given a non-empty totally ordered set such that it has neither maximum nor minimum element, has dense order, is complete and contains a countable dense subset, then there exists an order isomorphism between the set and the real line.

This means that this axiomatic theory cannot be taken as the sole foundation of mathematics, especially after what we will say shortly about Godel's results.

There is instead an undecidable result from Peano's arithmetic but demonstrable in the axiomatic theory of sets and it is Goodstein's theorem. The base-n inheritance notation (where n is a natural number) is given by the following expression:

$$a_k n^k + a_{k-1} n^{k-1} + \ldots + a_0$$

Where all coefficients a are between 0 and n-1.

We define the dilation operation as the substitution of the indices n+1 by those n in a base n+1 inheritance notation.

The Goodstein sequence is thus defined by recurrence using the dilation operation (denoted by d):

$$G(1, m) = m$$
$$G(n+1, m) = d(G(n, m)) - 1$$

Goodstein's theorem states that all Goodstein sequences reach zero, whatever the starting value.

A first axiomatic set theory that goes beyond ZFC is the Tarski-Grothendieck theory which is not conservative with respect to ZFC.

Many axioms are equivalent to those of ZFC, for example:

1) Ontology: logical quantifiers make sense only on sets.
2) Extensionality axiom: two sets are identical if and only if they have the same elements.
3) Axiom of the empty set: there exists a set of which no other set is an element.
4) Axiom of regularity: no set is an element of itself and circular chains of belonging are not possible.
5) Replacement axiom: the image of a function is a set.

The real novelty is given by Tarski's axiom: for every set x there exists another set y such that x belongs to y, for every z belonging to y then every subset of z is an element of y and the set of parts of z is an element of y, moreover every subset of y whose cardinality is less than that of y is an element of y.

This axiom implies the axioms of the couple, of the power set, of the union, of the infinite and of the choice.

This means that the Tarski-Grothendieck axiomatic theory is stronger than the ZFC one.

A conservative extension of ZFC is the axiomatic set theory of Von Neumann-Bernays-Godel which however changes ontology with respect to ZFC.

The fundamental difference from ZFC is the distinction between proper class and set.

The belonging of an individual A to another individual B denotes A as a set and B as a class (in this axiomatization sets are denoted by lowercase letters, classes by uppercase ones).

It is called universal class V, the class of all sets.

The binary relation denoting the set a as representing the class A is called representation. Classes that have no representation are called proper classes.

We can define five axioms about sets (extensionality, coupling, union, power, infinity) in a similar way to what is done by the ZFC scheme; moreover, there are two axioms (extensionality, regularity) defined on classes.

It is typical of this axiomatization to introduce two new axioms about classes:

1) Size limit: for each class C, there exists a set x such that x=C if and only if there is no bijection between C and class V of all sets.

2) Scheme of class comprehension: for every formula not containing quantifiers between classes, there exists a class such that the formula explicits every set belonging to the class.

Godel's theorems

One of the most advanced results of contemporary mathematical logic is given by the enunciation of Godel's theorems.

Godel's completeness theorem establishes a correspondence between semantic truth and logical provability in first order theories.

The theorem states that a deductive system for first-order predicate logic is complete, furthermore all provable formulas are logically valid.

From this it follows that a formula is logically valid if and only if it is demonstrable.

Generalizing this theorem, it can be said that for every first-order theory and for every closed formula in the first-order language, there exists a formal deduction of the formula starting from the theory if and only if the formula is verified in every model.

A consequence of this theorem is that the logically valid and provable formulas of a theory are a countable quantity.

It should be noted that second-order logics do not have a standard semantic completeness theorem: it is possible to construct correct deductive systems in second-order logic, but such systems are not complete.

Godel has two incompleteness theorems.

The first states that, in any mathematical theory that contains an arithmetic, there exists a formula such that, if the theory is consistent, then neither the formula nor its negation is provable in the theory.

In other words, for any axiomatic theory of natural numbers it is possible to construct a syntactically correct proposition which can neither be proved nor disproved within the theory.

The second theorem states that, in any mathematical theory that contains arithmetic, if the theory is consistent, it is not possible to prove its consistency within the theory.

In other words, no coherent system can be used to demonstrate its own coherence.

It is therefore not possible to define the complete list of axioms which allows to demonstrate all truths, as done by Peano for arithmetic or by ZFC for set theory.

Furthermore, it is not possible to solve Hilbert's program ie prove the consistency of all mathematics.

Godel's theorems therefore put very specific limits to mathematical logic and to the very concept of mathematics and science that we have in the contemporary vision.

We call Godel numbering a function which assigns to each production of formal language a single natural number called Godel number.

One of the consequences of Godel's theorems is Tarski's indefinability theorem.

Given a language of first-order arithmetic, the theorem states the impossibility of the set of Godel numbers of true statements in the standard structure being defined by a formula of first-order arithmetic. In other words, arithmetic truth cannot be defined within arithmetic itself.

Paradoxes and antinomies

In mathematical logic, paradoxes and antinomies are of particular importance.

The paradox is a proposition that is possibly proved and logically coherent, but which goes against common intuition; the antinomy is a real logical contradiction; many times, however, these terms are used interchangeably. There are logical paradoxes of antiquity (for example Zeno's paradox), here we will explain the main paradoxes of modern logic.

Using naïve set theory, Russell's antinomy can be stated: the set of all sets that do not belong to themselves belongs to itself if and only if it does not belong to itself. The logical contradiction of this proposition is evident and yet the statement is formally correct in naive set theory. This antinomy led to the overcoming of the naive theory of sets through axiomatic theories and from here the solution was reached thanks to Godel's incompleteness theorems.

A generalization of Russell's antinomy in linguistic terms is given by the antinomy of heterologicity, also called Grelling-Nelson. This antinomy demonstrates how Russell's antinomy holds for non-mathematical languages as well.

Other reformulations of Russell's antinomy are the paradoxes of the librarian and the barber.

Godel's incompleteness theorem has also given solutions to the so-called semantic paradoxes, such as Richard's and Berry's.

The Burali-Forti antinomy demonstrates how constructing a set of all ordinal numbers leads to a contradiction. This antinomy is overcome in the axiomatic theories of sets by not allowing the existence of a set constructed according to the logical scheme "all sets having a certain property".

The Banach-Tarski paradox, also called paradox of the doubling of the sphere, states that, using the axiom of choice, it is possible to subdivide a sphere in three-dimensional space into a finite and unmeasurable set of pieces, reassembling them by means of rotations and translations in such a way to obtain two spheres of the same radius as the original sphere. In other words, a three-dimensional Euclidean sphere is equidecomposable with two copies of itself.

The finite and non-measurable set is the Vitali set which is invariant under translations and is not measurable in any measure. This set is constructed starting from the interval [0,1] of real numbers and defining, within it, an equivalence relation if the difference between two numbers is a rational number; the set of all equivalence classes of this relation consists of an uncountable infinity. Then the axiom of choice states that there exists a set which contains a representative of each class and this set is the Vitali set.

Other logical systems

There are other types of logic than what has been presented so far.

Natural deduction represents and codifies a deductive system, therefore without axioms and with a series of inference rules dependent on primitive connectives.

It should be noted that, in the face of Godel's incompleteness theorems for axiomatic systems, deductive systems are the correct basis for mathematical proof and for scientific knowledge.

An inference rule can be introduced or eliminated for each logical constant and is divided into two parts: the premises or hypotheses, which are placed before the rule itself, and the conclusions or theses, which are placed after it.

Natural deduction is the basis of both minimal and intuitionistic logic, while the main assumptions are those of the principles of identity and the excluded middle, already introduced in elementary logic.

Intuitionistic logic is also called constructive logic and assumes that every statement must be demonstrated to be considered true.

For example, the principle of the excluded middle is not considered valid in this logic because it is not justifiable and therefore intuitionistic logic is not based on the concept of truth, but on that of justifiability.

In this logic, a correct demonstration is not the one which preserves the validity from the hypotheses to the thesis, but it is the one which preserves its justifiability.

Another example of a classical tautology rejected by this logic is that of the double negative.

This logic finds ample space and great applications in computer programming.

Modal logic expresses how a proposition can be true or false.

The basic modal operators are the one expressing necessity, denoted by a square, and the one expressing possibility, denoted by a diamond.

The two operators are linked together by the double negation: applying the operator of necessity (or probability) to a proposition is equivalent to applying the negation of the operator possibility (or necessity) on the negation of the proposition.

The aletic modalities are those connected to the truthfulness mode of a statement and are divided into logical possibility, physical possibility and metaphysical possibility.

There are also epistemic modalities characterized by the knowledge and belief modal operators, denoted by the capital letters K and C.

The belief operator satisfies some basic principles, including that of introspection, that of epistemic non-contradiction, that of non-implication of the truth and that of the impossibility of the non-certainty of doubt.

The operator of knowledge, in turn, satisfies the principle of implication of truth, of implication of belief, of epistemic non-contradiction and of introspection.

There are also time and duty modes to characterize such operators based on time and the concept of leave.

It is also possible to axiomatize a modal logic, for example Kripke's logic foresees all the axioms of first order logic with the addition of an axiom concerning necessity and one concerning the distribution of the modal operator necessity.

Other modal logics also use the transitive, symmetric, serial, and Euclidean properties.

In modal logic, Barcan's formula (with its inverse) represents a relationship between quantifiers and modal operators: the operator of necessity can be exchanged with the quantifier it defines "for each" and vice versa.

Dynamic logic is an extension of modal logic and in fact is also referred to as multimodal.

The necessity and possibility operators are generalized to a number of propositions and not to a single statement.

The axiomatizations of this logic are very similar to those of modal logic, also managing to derive compound inference rules and to axiomatize the classic visions of modus ponens and modus tollens.

Particularly important in this logic is the statement of assignment which, starting from a scheme of axioms, allows the construction of arithmetic and elementary algebra operations.

Furthermore, in dynamic logic, each proposition is associated with an action called test which allows to derive the normal laws of logical implication and to reduce the quantification operator to the concept of causal assignment.

First-order logic derives from dynamic logic by simply assigning to an action the value of the test on the single proposition.

Dynamic logic applied to normal first-order logic is called propositional dynamic logic and allows a great leap forward, above all to bring the field of logic to the application level of artificial intelligence.

Descriptive logics represent a family of formalisms which, through relevant concepts in the domain of application, specify the properties of objects and individuals belonging to this domain, called the world.

These logics, starting from an ontology, use a representation of knowledge through the so-called reasoner, obtaining explicit concepts from the ontology itself.

There are various descriptive logics, in particular they make use of the possibility of using the negation operator, the possibility of defining hierarchies, the possibility of enumerating objects and individuals, the possibility of introducing the inverse role of operators, the possibility of introducing conjunction operators, quantifiers and cardinalities.

The generic logics in standard T are logics characterized by an application T defined in [0,1] x [0,1], which sends values in [0,1], having the commutative, associative, monotonicity and endowed properties of null element and of the identity one.
In this logic it is possible to define the connectives of conjunction and disjunction on the basis of the T norm.

Polyvalent logics are extensions of classical logic in which the principle of the excluded middle does not apply as there are more truth values than the classic true and false.
For example, a multipurpose logic proposed by Post was a logic with three truth values: true, false and problematic.
There are also logics with infinite truth values, such as Godel's multipurpose logic:

$$x \wedge y = \min(v(x), v(y))$$
$$x \vee y = \max(v(x), v(y))$$
$$\bar{x} = 1 \Leftrightarrow v(x) = 0$$
$$\bar{x} = 0 \Leftrightarrow v(x) \neq 0$$

Or the multipurpose product logic:

$$x \wedge y = v(x)v(y)$$
$$x \vee y = v(x) + v(y) - v(x)v(y)$$
$$\bar{x} = 1 \Leftrightarrow v(x) = 0$$
$$\bar{x} = 0 \Leftrightarrow v(x) \neq 0$$

In these logics, the double negative is not valid.
These logics are extensions of the Boolean one.

Among the multipurpose logics, fuzzy logics have a primary importance, i.e. logics whose degree of truth of a proposition can be between 0 and 1.
These logics base their foundations on the definition of fuzzy sets and are fundamental for the modern evolutions of finance, statistics, neural networks, chaos theory, numerical and electronic calculation as well as in the vast majority of scientific applications.
Fuzzy set theory is an extension of classical set theory in which the principles of non-contradiction and the excluded middle are not valid,

substantially rejecting, like all polyvalent logics, the bivalence of truth and the semantic paradoxes generated over the centuries, as the classic example of establishing the veracity of the following proposition "this sentence is false". In a fuzzy logic the truth values are defined according to the Zadeh operators:

$$x \wedge y = \min(v(x), v(y))$$
$$x \vee y = \max(v(x), v(y))$$
$$\bar{x} = 1 - v(x)$$